MW00423416

Modern Watch and Clock Repairing

Modern Watch

AND

Clock Repairing

P. Buford Harris

Professional / Technical Series

Nelson Hall

Publishers

ISBN: 0-911012-05-2

Library of Congress Catalog Card Number 73-77479

For information address Nelson-Hall Company, Publishers,
325 West Jackson Blvd., Chicago, Ill. 60606.

Manufactured in the United States of America.

Preface

Until within the last few years the home of watchmaking was Europe, specifically Switzerland. For this reason, practically all books written in English on the subject of horology came from England. They had a European flavor and viewpoint.

In fact, up to the time this one-volume course was written, there was no American book on watch and clock repairing that offered a systematic treatment of the trade for beginners and watchmakers. This is a pioneering effort.

And it is about time, too! Modern watchmaking is typically American. Switzerland now imports American-made machines to make watch parts. The largest watch factory in the world is in America.

My aim in writing this course is to teach you how to understand modern watches and clocks . . . teach you how to locate troubles . . . repair . . . clean . . . adjust . . . and do all jobs the average watchmaker is daily being called upon to do. Necessary information on tools and materials is included.

The plan of instruction is simple. In the writing of this series of lessons I thought of myself as a teacher and you a student. We are working together at a bench. I start a job from the very beginning and talk to you about it and explain every move I make. You, in turn, are to do the same operation after you have watched me do it.

Explanations are detailed and language is plain. I have tried to "talk" rather than "write."

If you will go to work seriously, following these instructions step by step, you will see that there is nothing mysterious about a watch. Viewed as a whole it looks extremely complicated to a beginner. But after you go to work on a watch and handle the various jobs logically, one after another, just as they are taught in the following pages . . .

you'll soon acquire the "know-how" and understand the various individual units and how they go to make up the whole.

* * *

The theories and principles of time measurement are fascinating but they probably confuse the beginner. To start in the field of horology properly I feel something more practical is better. This is why the first lesson of this course gets you to work on a real watch immediately. After you have mastered the elements of watchmaking I suggest you learn its absorbing history and the fundamentals of time recording. You'll enjoy it.

One of the special advantages of this trade is something apart from making a good, steady income. When you are a watchmaker you are somebody in your community. There is prestige in this vocation. And while this by itself would not be sufficient reason to enter the field . . . when it is something you get over and above substantial earnings it is very much worth while.

Every wide-awake man is ambitious to improve his family's place in this world. For the sake of his wife and children a man should acquire a good reputation and prepare himself for the kind of position that will make them proud of him.

Contents

Acknowledgments

I take this opportunity to thank the firms in the watch trade that helped in the preparation of this course. If in some instances proper credit has not been given it in no way implies I am not deeply grateful and in their debt.

Many of the drawings and illustrations throughout this course were generously furnished by these concerns. Especial thanks are due the following companies for their unusual cooperation:

C. & E. Marshall Co., manufacturers, jobbers, importers of jewelers' tools, materials and supplies; 1445 W. Jackson Blvd., Chicago, Ill.

Hamilton Watch Co., Lancaster, Pennsylvania.

Time Products, Inc., 580 Broadway, New York City. Distributors of the Watchmaster rate recorder.

P. BUFORD HARRIS

Introduction

The purpose of this new home-study course is two-fold. First, to prepare you to make money as a practical watch and clock craftsman. Second, to give you a basic training in horological instruments as a preparation for the study of naval and aviation instruments, and other precision scientific instrument work.

Opportunities in this field are almost limitless for one aggressive enough to go after them.

It is usually possible to start making money almost at once while you are learning. Spare-time work in your own home takes very little capital . . . only the cost of your working equipment. And besides the income it brings it also helps you master the trade faster than would otherwise be possible.

Progressive steps upward as you are financially able are rather easy, as the main asset of a watchmaker is always his knowledge. Many rich jewelers started with a small space in a front window rented from another concern.

Age or physical condition has little to do with your rate of progress if you are determined to make a success of yourself.

You can start as small as you like . . . doing home-work on your own . . . or take-out work in your own home for established watch and clock concerns. You might prefer a free-lance type of work where you are free to move about as you like rather than establishing a business of your own. In either case, your knowledge of practical watch repairing is a valuable asset you carry around with yourself . . . an asset no one can take from you.

It is a vocation you can get into with the assurance that its importance is increasing each year. And you have a lifetime trade in which real experts are not generally discarded as soon as a younger man with more muscle applies for a job.

This self-instruction course offers you a thorough, systematic training in far less time than the apprenticeship method. If you have normal intelligence, ambition and the drive of most self-educated men you'll make the grade.

A young man who spends 5 years of his life sweeping floors and polishing doorknobs in a jewelry shop to learn watch repairing pays too high a price. The kind of fellow who is going to get ahead anyway . . . can travel much faster by a wise use of his time through self-study.

This method of learning develops initiative, self-reliance and those other qualities that are characteristic of successful men. It is of utmost importance that you get into the habit of making your opportunities rather than waiting for them.

The technical aspects of horology are so vitally essential to today's world that this knowledge is excellent basic training for any mechanically minded young man. Your knowledge of watchmaking can give you a fine start in many other professions doing precision work. Lens and shutter work on cameras, for instance . . . radio dial work, aircraft instruments, pressure gauges, etc.

In fields not so closely connected with watchmaking you will be able to use your knack of handling small parts, tools and appliances. You can use your knowledge of mechanical principles, of gears, etc.

But most important and of immediate concern, apply yourself and this course will teach you the practical art and science of repairing watches and clocks. You will enjoy it immensely, as a profession, as a hobby, as a basic technical training.

How to Study This Course

This course is comparatively easy and any man with average intelligence and interest in mechanical things should be able to master it by himself.

But in order to learn watchmaking in the shortest possible time and with the least lost motion there are a few fundamental rules of study you should follow.

You must remember, first of all, that this is a one-volume course to be studied. It is not just a book to read. Studying means slow, thoughtful mastering of facts, one after another. It cannot be done as rapidly as ordinary reading. And you've got to think your way through.

This is the difference between reading to kill time and reading to gain knowledge. The difference between studying a school textbook and studying a practical course to acquire useful knowledge is this: while studying the course you are expected to do something besides absorb the printed word.

Step after step, this course instructs you exactly what to do and how to do it. You want to learn watchmaking so it is expected that you will do the practice work in the following pages.

The lessons are arranged in their order of difficulty. In the first lesson you are introduced to the trade and no previous knowledge on your part is assumed. But in order for you to understand the second lesson you must have mastered lesson one. And it goes on that way through the entire course. One lesson leads gradually into the next. No lesson is hard to understand if you know everything that has gone before.

Reading, reviewing and rereading is necessary. Do the watch or clock jobs explained in each lesson. Understand every sentence, every word. Until you do you are not ready to pass on to the next lesson.

There is an old Chinese saying that "A . . . journey . . . of . . . a . . . thousand . . . miles . . . is . . . made . . . step . . . by . . . step."

A watch has some 150 parts and this course introduces you to all of them. But you are not to concern yourself with the complete watch until the lessons bring you to that point. Learn about each unit or group of units as you come to it. Before you realize it all these individual scraps of knowledge will begin to fit together in your mind like a jigsaw puzzle. Simply do what the course instructs . . . follow directions carefully . . . and you will soon be repairing watches and clocks without the aid of your lessons.

To be quite accurate, this course teaches you to be a "watch repairer" not a "watch maker." Today watches are made by machines. When you need a new part it is far quicker (and, therefore, more profitable) to order it by number from your supply house, which in turn orders from the factory that made the watch you are repairing.

In a few instances, however, you might be unable to buy a machine-made part for an unusual Swiss movement. This course teaches you how to make some of these parts to take care of just such emergencies.

But in general you can feel that everything these lessons teach is of immediate practical importance. You might not understand the importance of each point while you are studying . . . but learn it anyway so you'll be prepared when you need the knowledge at some later time. Every effort was made to streamline this course by weeding out all the irrelevant, and including nothing that did not aid toward the ultimate goal of teaching you modern watch and clock repairing.

A word of thanks to Mr. P. Buford Harris who created and arranged this fine course. In all our wide experience in the home-study field we have never found a course so well designed for self-instruction.

The easy simplicity with which Mr. Harris explains what might otherwise be complicated topics indicates his own mastery of the subject. He is today working at his trade, which accounts for the down-to-earth, practical way he makes plain the workings of a watch.

Mr. Harris is a top-flight craftsman and his teaching procedure is sound. He has studied the working methods of hundreds of successful watchmakers and jewelers in the course of his 20 years experience as an expert watchmaker, traveling salesman, horological writer, store owner and manager.

NELSON-HALL CO.

Modern Watch and Clock Repairing

Tools, Equipment and How to Take Down a Watch

The quickest way to learn watchmaking is to begin by repairing a watch.

If you were to attend one of the better schools of watchmaking, you would spend long hours learning to use the file, to turn things on the lathe. You would do many things that watchmakers are seldom required to do. The object, of course, is to teach you to handle your tools. It is good training.

But in a streamlined course designed to enable you to start earning money at the earliest possible moment, we shall begin with the watch itself. And since we get no monthly tuition from you, there is no reason to keep you any longer than absolutely necessary.

First you will need a watch repair bench. (See illustration 1)

If a standard bench is not available, have one made approximately 38 inches high, 22 inches deep, 40 inches long. Each side should contain several drawers for holding tools.

Illustration 3 shows a good set of Beginners' Tools. You may start with this or get the tools suggested just as you need them. You will also need a comfortable chair, a good bench lamp. Since you must sit for long hours, keep down fatigue by making yourself as comfortable as you can.

You will also need two pairs of good tweezers, one with a very fine point for hairsprings. (See illustration 8) At least three screwdrivers of different sizes. One very fine blade, one medium blade, and one blade large enough for pocket watch screws.

Among the heavy items, you will need a good lathe, lathe motor, and a good staking tool.

With these things, you are now ready to begin the study of the watch movement.

From some jeweler, pawn shop, or watchmaker friend, secure a good used 16 size Hamilton watch movement. Get one in as good condition as possible, preferably a 17 jewel movement.

Since Hamilton does not make a cheap watch, you will also need a good 16 size 7 jewel movement of some other make. But for the moment we will confine ourselves to the 16 size Hamilton. The Hamilton has been chosen as our model because it is as nearly perfect as any watch made today, and it is so constructed that it is easy to get to and repair any part.

★   ★   ★   ★   ★

The first thing we do is take the movement from the case. This is done by removing the case screws — the large-headed screws opposite each other on the very outside of the movement, holding it in the case. When they are out, pull the stem into "setting" position, and let the movement drop out into your hand, from the back.

Place the movement on the correct size movement holder. Use a bench key (See illustration 2) to relieve the tension on the mainspring.

This is done by winding slightly with the bench key, and with the left hand holding the point of a screwdriver blade against the click so it releases the ratchet wheel. Let the spring down gently, controlling it with pressure on the bench key as it turns backward in your hand. (See illustrations 4 and 5)

Study these illustrations carefully to familiarize yourself with the various parts of the watch. Refer to these illustrations frequently as you go along.

Now turn the movement over. With a hand remover (See illustrations 6 and 7) remove the hour and minute hands. This tool is operated by pressing the button on the end of the handle until the jaws open. Slip them gently under the hour hand and press downward on the handle. Before attempting to remove hands, protect the dial with a piece of celluloid or tissue paper slit and slipped underneath the hands.

The dial is now removed by releasing approximately two rounds on each of the three dial feet screws, evenly spaced around the main plate. Be certain all feet are free before attempting to move the dial upward and off. Now tighten the dial screws again so they will not come out while the watch is being handled.

Next use the tweezers to lift off the hour wheel. The pinion im-

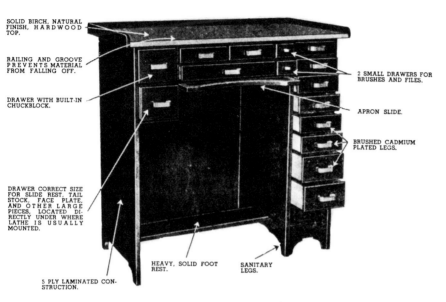

SOLID BIRCH, NATURAL FINISH, HARDWOOD TOP.

RAILING AND GROOVE PREVENTS MATERIAL FROM FALLING OFF.

DRAWER WITH BUILT-IN CHUCKBLOCK.

DRAWER CORRECT SIZE FOR SLIDE REST, TAIL STOCK, FACE PLATE, AND OTHER LARGE PIECES, LOCATED DIRECTLY UNDER WHERE LATHE IS USUALLY MOUNTED.

5 PLY LAMINATED CONSTRUCTION.

2 SMALL DRAWERS FOR BRUSHES AND FILES.

APRON SLIDE.

BRUSHED CADMIUM PLATED LEGS.

HEAVY, SOLID FOOT REST.

SANITARY LEGS.

Illustration 1—New type watchmaker's bench.

mediately underneath the hour wheel is the cannon pinion. There are several ways of taking it off. Perhaps the safest way for a beginner is to use a round Pin Vise. Place the jaw over the pinion, tighten it, and turn the pinion a round or two while lifting upward at the same time. Be certain to exert a straight and even pull, as any side pressure might break the center post on which the pinion operates.

The Hamilton floating stud is the safest of all hairspring studs. It makes hairspring replacing possible without recentering and releveling.

To remove the balance and hairspring, first unscrew the two stud cap screws just enough to release the stud. Do not pick the stud out from under the cap, as this will put a short kink in the hairspring at the regulator pins. You want to avoid any injury to the hairspring.

Unscrew the balance cock screw and lift the cock up and away from the movement so that the balance will not catch on the center wheel and stretch the hairspring. The balance is now suspended by the hairspring. By tilting the cock toward the stud side, the stud will fall out. Tighten stud screws down again.

Now using your eye loupe (See illustrations 9 and 10) carefully

examine the balance assembly. You will find it consists of the following: balance cock; balance wheel; hairspring; roller table; roller jewel,
etc. Impress these things on your mind. Get a vivid picture of each
part and its proper relation to each other part. This is important.

To continue taking the watch down, remove the other plate screws
and the screws holding both main wheel and ratchet wheels. The
main wheel screw is a left hand thread. Use your tweezers to lift the
two sections of the top plate off the train wheels. Before removing the
wheels themselves, note carefully just how each fits into the plate; how

Illustration 2—
Nickel plated bench key equipped with spring device to hold square stationary while using.

they are situated in relation to each other and to the watch as a whole.
Remember these details. Next remove the screw from the pallet bridge
and lift it from the plate. The pallet will now lift out.

The wheels of the watch from the mainspring barrel down to the
escape wheel, are called the "train wheels", or the train. Before proceeding, trace the power from the mainspring barrel down through
the entire train to the pallet fork, and then from the pallet fork to the
balance wheel by way of the roller jewel and hairspring.

Examine the mainspring barrel. Note how it is closed up completely. To remove the mainspring, insert the point of a small screwdriver under the head at the opening made for that purpose, and raise
the head upward. Run the screwdriver blade around the barrel underneath the head until it comes off freely.

Using the tweezers again, turn the barrel arbor one-half turn clockwise and lift it out of the barrel. Now grasp the barrel firmly in the
left thumb and fingers and with the tweezer pull gently on the inside
end of the mainspring. After it has started coming out of the barrel,
let it come out in your hand. Do not let the barrel get away from you
in this process, as considerable pressure is placed on the barrel by
way of reaction as the spring comes out.

Lift the train wheels out one at a time, beginning with the center wheel and working down to the escape wheel. Note the size of the wheel and where each one goes.

Examine the setting assembly carefully before removing it. Notice how each piece fits into or onto the other. Also note the general appearance of the whole assembly. Lift it out and separate the various pieces, making a mental note of the correct position of each one; which comes off first; which second, etc. They must go back in reverse order.

Cleaning a Watch by Hand

The watch is now taken down and is ready for cleaning. If you are fortunate enough to have the use of a cleaning machine, the procedure will be somewhat different from that suggested here. In another lesson machine cleaning will be explained. Here, for the benefit of the majority who do not have the use of cleaning machines at this stage of the course, we will instruct in the best methods of hand cleaning.

You may not be in position to get a cleaning machine for some time, but prepared cleaning solutions may be had and may be used for hand cleaning. If you prefer a more economic solution, it may be mixed right in your own home as follows:

To six parts distilled water, add one part 16% ammonia water, one part Castile soap. If pure Castile soap is not available, use any good pure soap such as Ivory. Shave it into very fine shavings and dissolve in water well before adding the ammonia.

Keep the solution tightly covered to avoid evaporation of the ammonia. Place enough in a glass container to completely immerse the largest pocket watch movement.

Take the disassembled watch and string it piece by piece on a strong wire such as a guitar string. When every piece that can be strung, except the balance wheel, is on the wire, loop the ends together so the parts cannot slip off while in the solution and place in the glass container.

Let the movement stay in the solution several minutes. Occasionally move the parts about, changing their positions and keeping the solution agitated. Should the ammonia content be too great, brass wheels and plates will turn dark. If this should happen, add more distilled water. If the solution is correctly mixed, the movement may be removed after several minutes and the plates and wheels will be clean and will have a new look. Hold them under a spigot of clear water until the cleaning solution has all been removed.

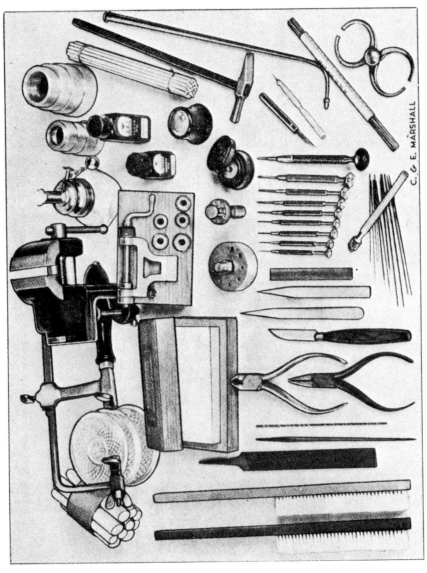

C. & E. MARSHALL

Illustration 3 —
A good selection of watchmaker's tools called the "Beginner's Outfit". Consists of 35 parts:
Plier, Black, Cutting 4½".
Plier, Black, Flat 4½".
Vise.
Oil Cup, Small Wood.
Hammer and Handle.
Alcohol Cup.
Alcohol Lamp.
Pegwood.
Pith.
Tweezer.
Tweezer.
Screw Drivers—Set of 8.
Brush, Soft.
Brush, ½ Hard.
Flat File 5½".
Round File, 4".
Marco Watch Oil.
Pivot Broaches.
Clock Screw Driver.
Eye Loupe, 2½".
Saw Frame.
Saw Blades (Medium)
Truing Caliper.
Glass Fountain Watch Oiler
Blow Pipe.
Anvil and Hub.
Oil Stone.
Screw Head File.
Broach Set on Card.
Hand Broaching Holder.
Mainspring Winder.
Aluminum Movement Holders.
Bench Knife.
Brass Wire—Tube.
Clock Oil.

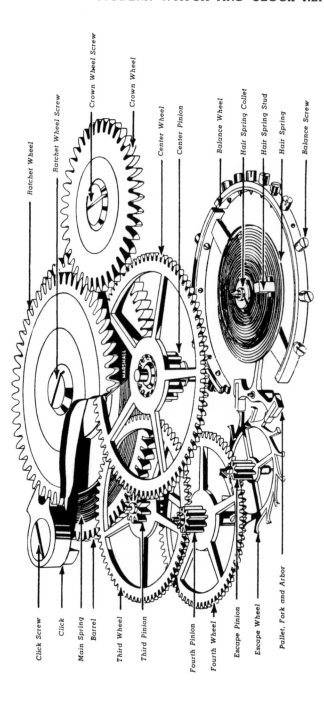

Illustration 4—Watch movement parts, showing relative positions and correct names.

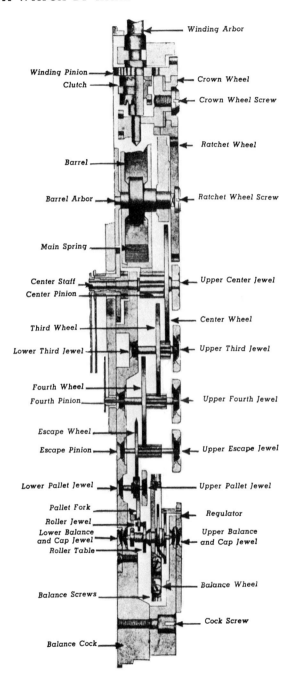

Winding Arbor

Winding Pinion
Clutch

Crown Wheel

Crown Wheel Screw

Ratchet Wheel

Barrel

Barrel Arbor

Ratchet Wheel Screw

Main Spring

Center Staff
Center Pinion

Upper Center Jewel

Third Wheel

Center Wheel

Lower Third Jewel

Upper Third Jewel

Fourth Wheel
Fourth Pinion

Upper Fourth Jewel

Escape Wheel
Escape Pinion

Upper Escape Jewel

Lower Pallet Jewel

Upper Pallet Jewel

Pallet Fork
Roller Jewel
Lower Balance
and Cap Jewel
Roller Table

Regulator

Upper Balance
and Cap Jewel

Balance Wheel

Balance Screws

Cock Screw

Balance Cock

Illustration 5—Watch movement parts. Side view of illustration 4.

During this solution removing process, it is well to have a good wash brush and a little baking soda handy. Wash the parts much as you would wash your teeth. When all parts are clean, immerse in a good quality rinsing solution. For this the prepared rinsing solutions will do an excellent job. Agitate them in the rinse until all water and cleaning solution are removed, then place near an electric heater to dry quickly.

In the center of your bench work plate, keep a small space clean for assembling purposes. Keep this spotlessly clean at all times. When taking the movement off the wire place it on the workbench so all pieces may be reached without loss of time or effort. Examine each part carefully with your eye loupe. See that all wheel teeth are clean. That there are no pieces of foreign matter caught in the pinion teeth. If the pinions are gummy or have pieces of foreign matter caught in them, go over them carefully with a sharpened pegwood. However, if the solution was properly mixed and the watch stayed in it long enough, all pinions should be clean and all plates should shine like new.

If there are rust spots in or on pinions, remove them before assembling. All rusty spots should be removed before the watch is cleaned, but occasionally such spots will be covered with other matter and cannot be detected until the watch has been cleaned.

The Secret of the Balance Assembly

We begin assembling the watch by cleaning and assembling the balance assembly. (See illustration 11) First, the balance pivots should be polished. This operation will be described in detail in a later lesson. However, here is where it should be done. Then remove the balance jewels and clean them.

This is done by laying the bottom plate on the movement rest, back side up. With a small screwdriver, remove the two jewel screws holding the balance jewels in position. Lay these screws aside where they will not get misplaced. Now use a jewel pusher — or a hard piece of watchmakers pegwood — to push the jewels out of the plate. There are two jewels. The one with the hole in the center, is called the "Hole Jewel". The other is the end stone, or cap jewel. Clean these two jewels carefully. If necessary take a piece of soft pegwood and scrub the jewels with it; then with a fine point, peg out the jewel hole.

This is done by sharpening the pegwood to a very fine point, inserting it in the jewel hole and rotating back and forth. When the jewel is clean, fit it over the lower balance pivot. See that it is large enough to allow the pivot to come completely through the jewel. The jewel should not be tight on the pivot. Nor should it be too loose. Tolerances here are very small.

If the pivot is the proper size and the jewel is large enough to play around on it freely, better exchange it for another jewel that fits a little more snugly. (Pivots and jewels will be discussed in detail in a later lesson.)

Assuming for the moment that the jewel is correct, we now place the jewel back into the plate from which it came (Note: The actual jewel is made of either sapphire or ruby and is placed in the center of a

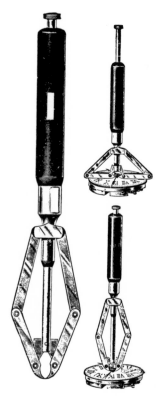

Illustration 6 — Hand remover. With this tool hands are easily removed from the movement.

Illustration 7 — Operation of hand remover. Prevents loss of hands by holding them in tool after removed.

gold or brass setting. This entire assembly is meant when we say jewel.) Now using a small oiler (See illustration 12) dip it in the oil cup on which a large drop of clean oil is kept daily. Change this oil each time you come to the bench. Keep it well covered when not in use. The oiler will pick up just a minute drop of oil. Touch the point of the oiler to the flat inside face of the cap jewel. Deposit just a small bubble of oil on the hole jewel. Press it down until it is flush with the plate. Be certain that the cap jewel is turned just as it was before being taken out. Not cocked on either side. Insert jewel screws.

Repeat this performance with the balance cock, except this time the hole jewel is tested with the top balance pivot. After the jewels are in their place, oiled, screws tight, you are ready to replace the balance wheel.

First, loosen the stud screws just a little. Lay the balance cock on its back, pick up the balance by the arm or rim and lay it over the balance cock so the pivot comes into the jewel. Using the balance wheel to control the hairspring, slip the hairspring stud into its slot, then lift balance cock up and over onto the plate.

Another method of doing this is to place the balance in its proper position on the plate, put the balance cock over it and tighten cock screw. Then move the balance around until the stud is under the stud holder. Catch the stud with the tweezers and place it under the cap, keep the overcoil on the outside of the regulator pins. Tighten the screws just a little — enough so the spring will not likely come out, but not enough to hold the stud tight.

Now place the overcoil between the pins and give it a very light swing. While swinging back and forth this way, the stud will find its natural position. When the balance comes to rest, tighten the screws on the stud.

If the hairspring was correctly shaped before being removed, and has not been mishandled in taking it out of the watch, the spring will need very little leveling or circling. Neither will it be necessary to change the regulator pins.

When the hairspring is level and true, stud screws tight, you are ready to proceed. See that balance wheel is free in every position. Now use the finger to turn the balance wheel one half round, and release. If it is free it should make approximately 60 strokes or revolutions before it comes to a dead stop. Repeat this performance on the other pivot. It should be equally free. Count the strokes and see that they are substantially the same on both pivots. Should one be somewhat less than the other, there is a reason. It must be found.

If the hairspring is level and touching nowhere, the trouble must be in the jewels. Perhaps one is not clean; or not properly oiled. Examine the jewels to see if they are flat. Test the pivots for any trouble there.

Illustration 8—Tweezers designed for small fine work.

One of the first tests should be for end shake. Use your eye loupe to observe the wheel while you grasp the cross arm with your tweezers and try moving it up and down, and sidewise. This is called testing the "end shake" and "side shake". Actually it is testing the tolerances in the jewels in both positions. There should be just enough tolerance for the wheel to be free in each position. No more. If there is more end shake or side shake than necessary, it must be corrected now. (See illustration 13)

Examine the jewels to see that they are properly seated in the plate and are not moving in any direction. See that jewels are tight. If the trouble is not in the jewels, remove the balance cock and see if some foreign matter has been left under it. If everything is found to be in perfect order, and still there is up and down shake that should be removed, there are several ways of doing it.

The best way is to exchange one or both of the hole jewels for another with a slightly thinner setting. If thinner jewel settings are not available, the original ones may be cut down just a little. This last process is a rather difficult operation, therefore, the following method is suggested instead.

If the end shake is not very great, remove the balance from the cock, and bend the cock slightly downward. A small amount of end shake may be adjusted this way without visibly affecting the cock. Catch the cock in the left thumb and fingers. Place a flat-nose, smooth-jawed plier over the end and bend slightly downward on it. Be careful with pliers here. Do not mar the cock. You must leave no plier marks. Try the balance frequently until the adjustment is correct.

When the end shake is correct, we go on with our adjustment of the balance assembly. Replace the balance on the cock and the cock on the plate. Let the roller jewel come to rest where it will. Now turn

Illustration 9—Pointed or pivot eye loupe.   Illustration 10 — Single lens eye loupe, hard rubber frame.

the cock away from you — that is, look at the balance assembly looking directly across the balance wheel toward the balance bridge, or cock. Again use the eye loupe to look at the position of the roller jewel, looking along the line of centers. In other words, looks at the roller jewel directly across the escape wheel pivot hole and on across the pallet arbor pivot hole directly to the balance pivot hole. These two holes are along an imaginary line of centers with the balance jewel.

When looking at the balance thus, the roller jewel should face you squarely, resting directly between the banking pins. (Refresh your mind on the movement as shown in illustrations 4 and 5, Lesson 1.) The hairspring should be level when viewed from every angle. When the balance is thus at rest, the overcoil of the spring should rest squarely between the regulator pins. It should be perfectly centered.

If the roller jewel does not face squarely between the banking pins when the balance is at rest, it may be corrected by moving the collet of the hairspring to the right or the left to obtain the desired effect.

This correction is made by lifting the balance assembly from the plate and holding the balance wheel with the fingers of the left hand while you insert a hairspring tool (See illustration 14) into the slot of the hairspring collet and move the collet on the staff. If the jewel is to be moved to the right, the collet usually goes to the left, and vice versa. A little experience will show you just how much to move it to get the desired result.

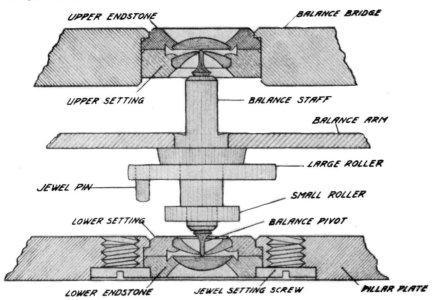

UPPER ENDSTONE   BALANCE BRIDGE

UPPER SETTING   BALANCE STAFF

BALANCE ARM

LARGE ROLLER

JEWEL PIN   SMALL ROLLER

LOWER SETTING   BALANCE PIVOT

LOWER ENDSTONE   JEWEL SETTING SCREW   PILLAR PLATE

Illustration 11—Improved balance jeweling.

Should the spring be untrue either in the flat or the round, now is the proper time to make such corrections. For the time being, however, we are more interested in learning the set up of the watch. Later the hairspring will be discussed in detail. Just remember when that time comes that in assembling a movement, now is the time to make all hairspring adjustments. For only when there is nothing on the plate except the balance assembly do you have an unobstructed view of the hairspring and roller jewel. If the balance is out of true, here, too, is the place to detect it and correct it.

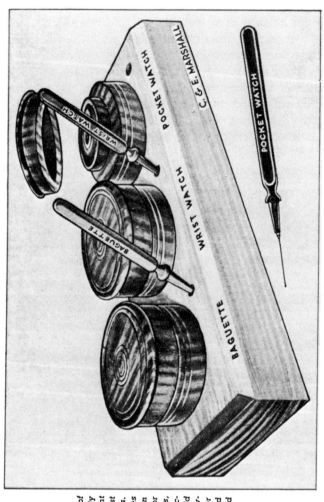

Illustration 12—Modern set of oil cups and oilers. Differently colored handles and different size points for Baguettes, Wrist Watches, and Pocket Watches. The proper oiling of watches and the preservation of oil on the bench is a very big factor in the repairing of watches, therefore should be given special attention. Watch oil should be kept in a neat, clean, covered oil container. The oiler also must be free from dirt and should be dipped in pithwood before using.

Assembly---How to put the Watch Back Together

Assuming that the balance is now in perfect working order, you are ready to assemble the complete watch. One of the first things to remember, is never let a bare finger touch any part of a freshly cleaned watch. Moisture from the hand leaves a spot that is not only unsightly but makes the watch tarnish quickly. This tarnish will soon turn to rust. Besides, finger prints give the watch a messy appearance. Avoid this at all times.

Occasionally you must touch the hairspring or some other part with the bare finger or hand. If you do so, clean it well afterwards. This moisture will cause the spring to rust, thus becoming unusable. Make every job as neat as it is good.

To prevent the fingers coming in direct contact with the plates and other parts as the watch movement is handled, use a good grade watch paper. If you have none available now, get some regular tissue paper. Cut it into squares approximately four inches in diameter. Learn to use it as you go along. Use it every time you must place a finger on the movement. If you must take the movement into your hand — and frequently you must — place the move-

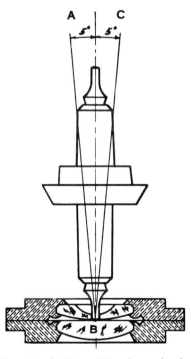

Illustration 13—Determining the angle of side shake in fitting a balance.

ment on a piece of tissue each time. Learn to handle each piece with tissue, and it will soon become second nature to do so.

Should you inadvertently get a fingerprint on one of the plates or steel wheels, take a piece of tissue and wipe it off very carefully. You get a lot of pride out of a job done well.

Now, with the tissue paper ready, return to the job of assembling the watch. First remove the balance assembly and lay it down in a safe, clean place on the bench. It is best to lay it down bottom side up. That is, with the balance wheel up and the cock on its back, thus the pivots do not pick up trash from the bench.

Lay the bottom plate upright on the movement holder. Use the tweezers to pick up the train wheels and place them in position. The escape wheel goes in first. See that the pivot is in its hole. Then comes the fourth wheel, followed by the third wheel and then the center wheel. If there are end stones on any of the plate jewels, they too must be cleaned and oiled just as the balance jewels were.

On the 16 size 17 jewel Hamilton on which we are now working there are no cap jewels in the plates. However, the 4th wheel has a long pivot for holding the seconds hand. This pivot goes down through the plate.

The train wheels are now in their respective positions on the plate. As this is your first time to do this, if you are not quite sure

Illustration 14 — Hair spring collet wrench for adjusting "beat" without removing balance.

of yourself, turn again to the large pictures of the train in Lesson 1 (illustrations 4 and 5) and check the watch against it.

Next comes the mainspring. Observe that the 16 size Hamilton has a T end spring. That is to say, the end brace is shaped like the letter T. Examine the barrel and you will find that the end of the T goes through both the barrel and the barrel head. The T holds the spring when it is wound, therefore, it must always be in place.

Use a mainspring winder (See illustrations 15, 16, 17 and 18). Select a barrel from the winder that will fit freely into the barrel of the watch.

Hook the inside end of the mainspring over the arbor of the winder and wind it into the winder barrel. Notice that if you hold the winder in the right hand and wind the spring with the left hand, the winding is clockwise. In short, it must be wound into the winder barrel in such manner that when it is pushed into the barrel of the watch the arbor

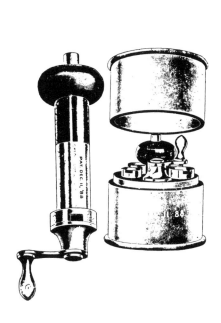

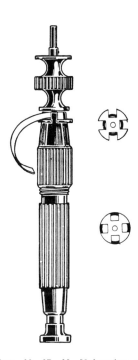

Illustration 15—Mainspring winder. Operated by hand entirely. No vise necessary. When a new spring is placed in the barrel, it should be wound up, and let down, 3 to 5 times, in order to "break it in", and to allow it to become adjusted to the barrel. It is then ready to be wound up to run the movement.

Illustrations 16, 17, 18—Mainspring winder, practical for average size bracelet watch, 6¾ to 8¾ ligne. Small round illustrations to the right show capacity of adjustable barrel. At the top, closed, 5½ M/M. Below, open, 8 M/M.

will catch the hole in the end. Now place the winder inside the watch barrel, work the T end into position, press the winder firmly into the barrel and release the spring.

Occasionally the brace slips out when the spring is released. Should this happen, it may be slipped back into position by using the point of a large screwdriver against the T. When you have turned it back to the hole and the T is into the slot properly, place the barrel arbor into the barrel. It must go in with the top side down, so the hook will contact the hole in the end of the spring.

As you go along you will find that other watches use many different types of ends on their mainsprings. But for the present we will confine our efforts to the 16 size Hamilton.

Now use a large oiler and place about three medium sized drops of oil on the mainspring. See that it flows completely around the coils so it will work its way onto each one. Take the barrel head and place it over the spring. Turn it until the brace slot comes over the brace, then force it into the barrel. This can best be done with a brush handle or some other object that has a smooth surface not hard enough to cause damage to the barrel. Press the head down evenly all around. It goes in with a gentle snap when it is properly done.

Examine it carefully to see that there are no high sides; that the teeth of the barrel are in good condition; that there are no pieces of foreign matter of any kind lodged between the teeth. When you are positive that everything is in shape, place the barrel in its position on the plate.

The power of the watch is now in order — the mainspring, of course, being the power house. Before completing the assembling we must place the setting assembly in place. No doubt it is now in several pieces laying on your bench and you have little idea how to proceed. Yet it is simple — if you remember how it was assembled when you took it down.

First take the arbor — that is the square bar with the pilot on the end — hold it between the thumb and first finger of the left hand and with your tweezer place the clutch over the arbor. Let the clutch slide down until it touches the fingers. Be sure the beveled teeth of the clutch are on the end away from the pilot. Now the winding pinion goes on the other end with the beveled teeth facing the beveled teeth of the clutch. Place the entire assembly in the watch. The clutch lever may be worked into the slot of the clutch by pulling out on the set lever.

You are now ready to place the upper plates into position. Here is a word of caution: — remember, in assembling a watch, never force anything. When it is right and in the correct position, it will go into place without being forced. If you force it, something is certain to break.

The bottom plate with the entire train in place is now on the bench before you. With your tweezers, take up the larger of the top plates. This goes over the mainspring barrel and cannot go on wrong. Lay it over and with the tweezers work the center wheel pivot into its jewel. Also see that the barrel arbor is in its bearing and that the setting assembly fits easily into the lower and upper plates. Warning: Before doing this, place some good watch oil on the four squares of the winding arbor and also under the winding pinion.

When everything is in place, the plate will automatically drop into position and down flatly on the bottom plate. If it should not do so, find what is holding it up. Correct the fault and notice how easily it fits into its proper place. Place at least one plate screw in the plate to hold it steady.

The last small triangular plate goes over the other three train wheels. If they do not fall into position when you place the plate over them, take a piece of tissue paper in your hand or wrap it around one finger and use this finger to hold the plate in place while you work the pivots of the train wheels into their jewel holes. Begin with the larger wheel and work down to the escape wheel. Remember: do not force the plate down. When the pivots are in the jewels correctly, the plate will slip down easily into position.

Place all plate screws into position and tighten them. Place a small drop of oil under the main wheel, also a drop under the hub of the mainwheel where it contacts the wheel itself. Then tighten the main wheel screw. Place a little oil around the arbor under the ratchet wheel. All friction parts should be oiled. The train may be oiled after it is assembled, but the winding assembly should be oiled as it is being assembled. All friction parts must have just a little oil.

Final Adjustments in Assembly---Oiling a Watch

We now have the watch assembled. If you care to do so, take it down again right now and assemble it without looking at the preceding lesson. You cannot do it too many times. Each time you learn something more about it and also teach your fingers and eyes to cooperate with each other. This coordination is absolutely essential in watchmaking.

When we left the watch in lesson four it was assembled and laying on the movement holder before you. Take up exactly where you left off. But now we are coming to some of the finer points; points where you must be both accurate and careful. First, let us continue oiling the watch.

Use your smallest oiler. Touch the point in the oil cup and touch it to each pivot of the train. Recharge the oiler after touching each pivot. Watch the action with your eye loupe to see that the oil runs from the point of the oiler to the pivot each time. You want just enough oil to remove the friction that the bearing would naturally have. It takes very little.

As stated before, there should be some oil at every point of friction. If there is no friction there at any time, there need be no oil.

After you have oiled all pivots of the train, wind the watch a few turns. Notice the noise of the winding. Also notice its freedom of action. If it makes a grating sound or feels rough either in winding or in the back action, place a little more oil on the point where the friction is located. It may be the arbor of the stem; it may be the mainwheel; it may be one of the springs holding the clutch lever in place. Locate the trouble wherever it is, and place just a little oil on it.

Do not flood the winding with oil. Too much oil may well be as bad as too little. A small amount at the proper place, will do the trick.

Now turn the winding a few turns and let the train run until it stops of its own accord.

Is the train free?

Does the escape wheel "back lash" a few turns when the train comes to a stop?

If the escape wheel "back lashes" — that is, reverses itself — several turns, the train is most likely free and well oiled. If there are any parts you have failed to oil, the train will probably be sluggish. Or it will make a noise when running. If much power is placed on

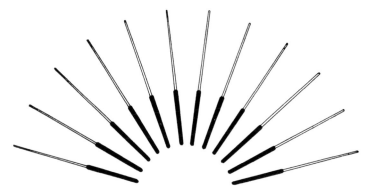

Illustration 19—Pivot broaches. Must be of best quality steel with accurately ground and tempered cutting edges.

the mainspring, perhaps the dry pivot will emit a slight whistling sound. This is a warning that there is a dry pivot somewhere that must be relieved with a touch of oil.

The train now being in order, next comes the pallet fork. It requires some care. See that pivots are clean and straight. Pallet stones should be clean. Pick it up with the tweezers and place it between the banking pins. Let the lower pivot drop into its jewel and move it just a bit back and forth to see that the pallet stones are free and not resting on top of an escape wheel tooth. Be certain that the lower pivot is in the jewel or pivot hole.

Also, use your tweezer to place the pallet bridge in place over the pallet fork. Work it down gently until the top jewel is over the top pallet pivot. See that the fork is free. Then press the pallet bridge gently into place.

When the bridge is in place and the screw tight, the watch should be wound several rounds. Test freedom of the fork now. If it is not free, let the power off the train at once and free the fork. Never try to free the fork with power on the train. After the fork is perfectly free and there is some power on the train, the fork should jump back and forth from banking pin to banking pin with just a slight touch with the tweezer.

Notice that as the fork jumps swiftly from one banking pin to the other, the escape wheel moves around just the distance of one tooth each time. Now move the fork slowly and watch the action of the escape tooth against the pallet stone. You will find that the fork has to

Illustrations 20, 21 — Hair-spring collet remover.

be moved with your power until the tooth slides down to the impulse face of the stone, then the fork jumps from the power of the train. This impulse action is what gives the watch its motion. In short, what makes Sammy run.

Now take up the balance assembly with the tweezers, turn it over and place it in the watch. Be sure to place the wheel in such manner that the roller jewel will come into the fork slot. That is, if the fork is resting on the right banking pin, the roller jewel comes in from the right side.

If you fail to get the jewel in the fork properly the watch will not run.

Lift the balance out and turn the roller jewel so as to bring it in on the same side as the fork. Do not catch the balance over the center wheel. It goes under the center wheel. Now drop the cock into position and see that the balance pivots are in place. The watch should now kick off. "Kick off" is not an official term, but all watchmakers use it to express the action of the watch starting to run of its own accord.

Warning: Never shake a watch to make it start.

If the roller jewel is placed correctly in the fork and yet it does not start, you may give the wheel just a slight movement with the hand or the tweezers. If everything is in proper order, even that will seldom be necessary.

You have now taken down a movement, cleaned it, and assembled it again. This is a good start. But only a start. You·must do this same operation several hundred times. It may sound monotonous, but it is not, really. It is a great adventure. Each watch is different, with different troubles and problems. There is something thrilling about locating these troubles and correcting them. Don't you feel that you have really accomplished something? Of course you do. You are not yet a watchmaker, but you are well on the way.

In the preceding lessons each move and operation has been described in great detail. This has been done because of your need for this extra help; you need a helping hand to guide you through these first groping operations. You are past that stage now. After you have repeated these operations several dozen times you will get the hang of it and will be able almost to do it without looking. That point of perfection is what we are working toward. That is how good you should be before going further into the study of horology.

★   ★   ★   ★   ★

At this stage almost every part of the 16 size Hamilton should be familiar to you. You should know its name; what it does; where it goes. And more important, you should know what particular function it has in the whole scheme of the watch.

In the lessons to follow, you shall not be bored with so much detail. Instead, you will be told how to perform a certain operation. You should be familiar enough with your tools and the workings of a watch to do the things you are told without every move being outlined.

Remember this: Only by doing these things over and over again and again, can you achieve that perfect coordination of eye and muscle so essential to the watchmaker. Now go on to the next lesson.

Handling the 7-Jewel Model

In the beginning you were instructed to get at least two 16 size movements for the purpose of following these lessons. One of these was to be a 7 jewel model. We are now at the point in our study that we come to the seven jewel movement.

No doubt by this time you have come to realize the function of the watch jewel. It is not just a precious stone. Rather it is a bearing. Its advantage is that it reduces friction and prevents wear. Under certain conditions a 7 jewel watch will keep as accurate time as a more highly jeweled watch. It will not give as long service, nor is it as well constructed as the more expensive watch.

To you the difference between a 7 jewel and a 21 jewel may best be described as the difference between a normal friction bearing and a ball bearing. Although the jewel is not strictly a ball bearing, it gives the same effect. In addition to the bearing of the watch, the jewel adds to the watch's appearance.

As further proof that jewels alone do not make a watch, with the advent of friction jewels a few years back a certain watch manufacturer began adding 14 plate jewels to his regular 7 jewel movements. It had none of the other qualifications of the regular 21 jewel watch. Therefore it was a success from neither a sales nor a timekeeping standpoint.

Do not get the impression that the 7 jewel movement is as good as the 21 jewel grades. It is not. But many things other than jewels enter into the value and quality of a watch movement.

To get back to our lesson, since we still have a few 7 jewel watches, we must learn to repair them. And one of the first operations is to close the pivot holes.

Take the movement in your hand and grasp an arm of the center wheel in your tweezers. With the mainspring wound so there will be some power on the train, press the center wheel backward just hard enough to overcome the power of the mainspring. As you do this, notice how the pivots of the train drop back and forth in their pivot holes.

Obviously, this much loss of motion in the train will cause considerable loss of power. Therefore, the watch cannot possibly give its best performance in this condition. But how to correct it?

We close the holes.

Before doing this, turn the watch over and you will find that the lower holes are not worn nearly so much. This is due to the wheels being on the top part of the pinions, therefore, the pressure is largely

Illustration 22—Bench anvil on block. The "V" slot is especially useful for removing pinions from wheels and permits a bearing close to wheel. The milled slots in top edges are useful for removing rivets from joints.

against the top pivots and pivot holes. Also, if you will notice the holes carefully you will find that they are worn egg-shaped. The reason is obvious.

A careful study of the situation before you proceed will lead to this conclusion: — the holes are egg-shaped; they must be round. Also, more important, they must be directly over the lower pivot holes after they are closed. In short, we must bring them back in line. Otherwise, the train wheels will be turning at an angle. The pinions will be setting at an angle. This will probably cause so much friction that the watch will not run at all.

This being true, we must try to close the hole so as to bring it back to round and also back to its original position. Sometimes this is not easily done.

First, of course we take the watch down and polish the pivots of all pinions.

Then select a flat faced stump for the stake. Measure the face of the stump against the small recess around the pivot hole on the BOTTOM of the plate. It must be just small enough to go into this recess and rest firmly on the plate immediately around the pivot hole. Place this stump in the stake.

Now select a ball faced punch. If the holes are very large and considerably out of round, select a ball faced punch with a small hole in the center. This hole should be somewhat larger than the pivot hole, but the face of the punch must be small enough to fit into the recess on the TOP side of the plate around the pivot holes.

Begin by placing the plate over the stump, putting the punch in the stake and bringing the punch down over the pivot hole. Hold the punch firmly and tap it lightly with a fiber headed mallet. As the size of the holes and the recesses on both top and bottom of the plates vary, change tools accordingly.

The metal of the plate is rather soft and does not need hard pounding to close it. Remember, too, that what you want to do is bring the

Illustration 23—Roller remover, can be used in any standard staking tool. Includes 3 punches and 4 stumps — will handle any roller made. This set is shown put up in covered wood box.

metal inward around the hole. A light tap will have a tendency to do this. A hard blow will spread the metal away from the hole. Bear this in mind when closing holes, and work carefully until the hole is somewhat smaller than the size of the pivot itself.

When the pivot hole is smaller than the pivot, you may stop closing the hole and begin opening it again.

This is done with the use of pivot broaches. (See illustration 19) These broaches cut very fast. Select one that has a fine point. Insert it in the hole and rotate back and forth slowly. Stop occasionally to try the pivot in the hole. Just as soon as the pivot will go into the hole and turn more or less freely, stop broaching.

Duplicate this operation with all the other pivot holes in all the plates. Take special notice of the center hole. Here is where the greatest power is concentrated, hence the most wear is likely to take place here. When all holes are broached, proceed to polish them.

There are many ways of polishing pivot holes. The one suggested here is used by many good watchmakers and may well be listed among the better ways.

With a sharp knife trim a piece of hard pegwood to a very fine point with four or five sides. Dip this point in oil and charge it with a good grade of diamantine or ruby powder.

Insert this point in each pivot hole and rotate it back and forth at a good rate of speed. Notice that at first the point doing the polishing becomes very black. You may have to sharpen and recharge with powder several times. After two or three applications the point no longer gets black with polishing. This may be taken as a sign that the hole is polished. Try the pivot to make sure the hole is large enough to permit freedom, and no larger.

After you have gone over all the pivot holes, set the train wheels back into position one at a time. Place the plate over each wheel and turn it to see that the pivots are free. Then place all wheels in the watch and test them for complete freedom.

If all is in working order, take the watch down again and clean it in the usual way. Examine it carefully as it is being assembled. Make certain the pivot holes are not still too large. Equally important they must not be so tight as to cause the train to bind. After the assembling, if there seems to be any binding at any point, start with the escape wheel and trace it right back to the center wheel itself. Somewhere along the way you will find the trouble.

Now oil the watch carefully. Each pivot must be oiled. Now that they are probably tighter than they have been since the watch left the factory, the oil may have to be worked down into the hole around the pivot. Do this by working the train back and forth with first one side up and then the other. If there is the slightest binding at any pivot, examine it for lack of oil or other causes.

When you are convinced that all is in first-class order, place the pallet fork in the watch and wind it a few rounds. Now test the train just as you did when you were looking for large holes before you took it down originally. Check the tolerances of the pivots now. It should be almost nil. If some holes have been broached too much, repeat the closing process until they are correct.

Meantime if you can get your hands on other 7 jewel movements, repeat this closing operation several times. You cannot do too much of it. Each new job brings experience; experience you must have. If no other 7 jewel movements are available, repeat this performance on the same one over and over until it will no longer stand the strain. Posterity might like to know how many times a watch will stand having its holes closed, reamed, and polished. Perhaps you can find out.

How to Select and Fit the Balance Staff

In order that this lesson be clear, understandable and of the greatest practical value to you, it is important that you approach its study ONLY after you have complete grasp of all previous lessons.

In fitting staffs, or for that matter any other part of a watch, you will be instructed to use only genuine material. You will be further instructed how to make such corrections as are necessary to make all parts fit. But there is one thing that you should never forget — NEVER USE A FILE ON A WATCH MOVEMENT. Remember this always. When you become a repairman, watches will be entrusted to your care only because they are out of order. The owner has money invested in his watch. Perhaps he is also sentimentally attached to it. He has a right to expect to get it back in better condition than when he left it with you. If you cannot return it in better condition, be certain you do not betray his trust in you, by actually doing it harm. When you see some of the jobs that come across the counter, you will better understand what I mean.

You have now come to that place in your study of horology — or watchmaking — that calls for your doing some actual repairs. Previous lessons have been largely to familiarize you with the working parts of the watch. Through knowledge and experience thus gained, you know the importance of the balance assembly. It is difficult to point out one particular part of the watch as being more important than the other. Each is important in its own particular sphere; each has certain functions to perform without which the whole would be incomplete. Hence all must be made as nearly perfect as possible.

It may be said safely that the balance wheel assembly — that is, the balance wheel, hairspring, staff, balance jewels, roller table and roller jewel, and escapement, — constitute the most important part of the watch. For here is where the smallest imperfection will do the greatest amount of damage. Everything else may be perfect and just one small fault with the balance assembly will throw the entire watch out of time. And when all is said and done, there is just one reason for repairing a watch — to make it keep TIME. If, for the smallest reason, you fail to do that, you have failed completely.

Keep the above statements in mind as you study this lesson. Open this volume on your work bench and actually proceed with the work

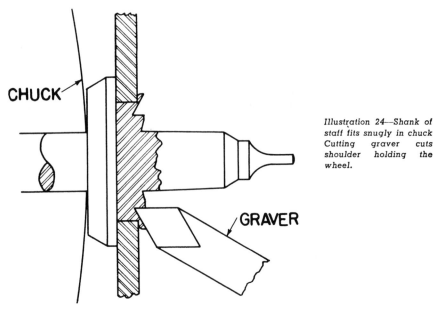

CHUCK

Illustration 24—Shank of staff fits snugly in chuck Cutting graver cuts shoulder holding the wheel.

GRAVER

as you read. Be certain you understand the instructions. Then do the job over and over until you can do it quickly and know why you do it. For you learn only by doing. You might memorize this series of lessons but without the practical knowledge which you gain by really doing them, the insides of a watch will forever remain a dark mystery. This lesson at best can tell you only what to do and how to do it. The work, you must do. Do not be discouraged if you sometimes fail. Only experience plus the knowledge imparted here will enable you to avoid failures.

In the first lessons, you were told every move to make and how to make it. If you have learned the previous lessons well, you should know the watch mechanism well enough to make minute details unnecessary. Hereafter, I shall merely tell you how to proceed with the work at hand, giving small details only when it is something you have not previously handled.

Still using the 16 size Hamilton watch as a model, we begin fitting a staff by first removing the balance assembly. Then remove the hands and dial, so we have access to the lower balance jewel.

Before the hairspring stud has been removed from the balance cock, take a small tweezer and with the tip make a small line on the

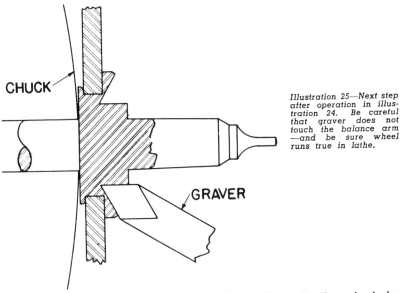

CHUCK

Illustration 25—Next step after operation in illustration 24. Be careful that graver does not touch the balance arm —and be sure wheel runs true in lathe.

GRAVER

wheel rim, centering the hairspring stud with the staff. Turn the balance over and do the same with the roller jewel. This facilitates putting them back on the balance in exactly the same position as before they were removed.

Using a hairspring remover (See illustrations 20 and 21) remove the hairspring from the balance. Do this by placing the balance on a bench block. (See illustration 22) Find hole large enough to accommodate the roller table, and let the balance rest flat on the block. Insert the hairspring remover into the collet slot. As it enters the slot it will spread the slot just enough that a few turns around the staff while lifting gently upward, should cause the collet to slide off the staff without trouble.

A very good tool for this may be made by grinding a needle down to the shape shown.

With roller remover (See illustration 23) remove the roller table. In the 16s Hamilton uses the two piece double roller and it is easily removed by tightening the Rex Stump underneath the large part of the table, placing the Rex Punch over the pivot and giving it a light tap with a small mallet. We now have only the staff and the wheel. You will notice the wheel is cut through on either side near the balance arm. There is a reason for this which will be more fully explained later. Just now it is useful to us only in truing and poising the balance.

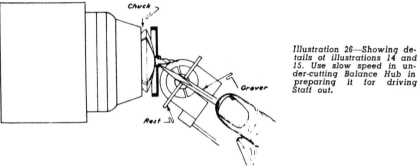

Illustration 26—Showing details of illustrations 14 and 15. Use slow speed in under-cutting Balance Hub in preparing it for driving Staff out.

You will also notice the staff is staked through the center of the wheel, holding it very firmly. This staff must be in the absolute center.

Examine the wheel closely now, noting which side is the top and which is the bottom. Notice, too, the difference in the ends of the staff. The top has two shoulders. A short one which holds the balance arm. A longer one which held the hairspring collet. The bottom shank is only slightly tapered and somewhat longer than the upper end, or that portion of the staff above the hub. Keep these details well in mind; they are all important.

Now to remove the staff from the wheel. This must be done without injuring the balance and without knocking it out of true, if possible. Any change in the balance wheel will mean a subsequent change in time keeping that will have to be corrected. Therefore, the fewer changes we make the fewer corrections will be necessary.

There are several approved methods of removing staffs. Each has certain advantages and certain disadvantages. The quickest method is to select a hole in your stake that will accommodate the hub of the staff with a very small tolerance; center this hole, place the balance over it and knock the staff out with a flat ended punch. The danger here lies in the staff being heavily bradded into the balance arm. In which case, you are certain to knock the wheel out of alignment, thus requiring a lot of time in truing. It could result in almost fatal injury to the balance wheel.

The method outlined below is not always the fastest, but on the whole it is safest. It is especially recommended for the beginner. First, because it does no damage to the balance; second, because it teaches

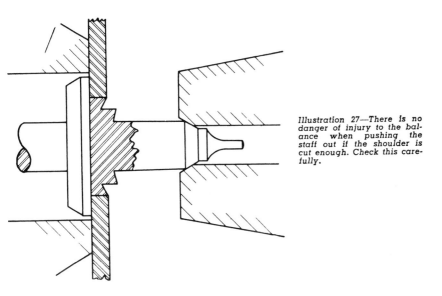

Illustration 27—There is no danger of injury to the balance when pushing the staff out if the shoulder is cut enough. Check this carefully.

you how to handle another tool — all of which helps along the road to perfect coordination of eye and hands.

To proceed, select a chuck that will fit snugly the shank of the staff. Place it in the lathe and see that the wheel turns true. Now use a cutting graver (See illustrations 24 and 25) to cut the shoulder holding the wheel. Be very careful to see that the graver does not touch the balance arm in the process. When the shoulder is cut enough, the staff may be pushed out without injury to the balance. (See illustration 27)

You now have a staff removed and are ready to select a new one. Use a genuine 16 size Hamilton staff, 17 Jewel grade. Push one end of the new staff into a block of firm pith. (Watchmaker's pith may be obtained from your supply house.) The pith will hold the staff while

you do all the fittings.   This way there is no danger of flipping the staff
from the tweezers, as will often happen otherwise.   Push this lower
shank into the pith.   Now the wheel may be tried to see if the hub fits.
Likewise, the hairspring may be set on the shoulder to see if the collet
is the correct size.   It is not necessary to push the spring all the way
down.   Whether it is too large, too small, or just right may be ascertained by placing it over the staff and noting how far down it drops.
If it drops down to the hub, it is too large and must be closed.

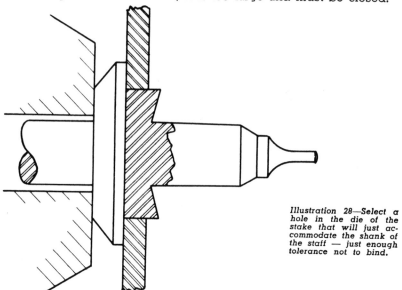

Illustration 28—Select a
hole in the die of the
stake that will just ac-
commodate the shank of
the staff — just enough
tolerance not to bind.

We make no claims that ours is the only correct method for closing
collets.   We submit it as one that has stood the test of time and is,
therefore, practical.   Remember, extreme care must be exercised with
whatever method used.   A quick and effective way is to lay the hairspring on a block, with a fine pair of cutting pliers grasp that part of
the collet protruding above the spring, and press it gently inward sufficiently to close the collet.   Take great care that the pliers do not grasp
the inner coils of the hairspring.

For the beginner, however, perhaps a better method is the round
Pin Vise.   The opening of the vise should be stepped down just large
enough to accommodate the collet.   Place the hairspring over the end
of the pin vise so the part of the collet below the spring drops into the
jaws of the vise.   Now tighten the vise slowly, closing the collet with

the jaws of the vise until it is sufficiently small to grasp the staff. In a job of this kind, always leave "well enough" alone. That is to say, when you are sure it will do, stop. There is a certain amount of danger involved here, as you will discover with experience.

Now reverse the staff in the block of pith, and try the roller table on the shank. It, too, should slip freely nearly all the way down to the shoulder of the staff. If it will just start on the shank, the shank is too large and must be cut down. This is done by placing the staff in the

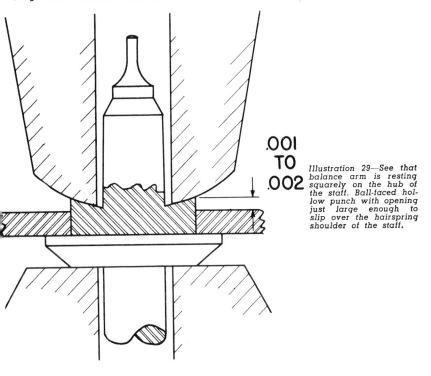

.OOl
TO
.OO2

Illustration 29—See that balance arm is resting squarely on the hub of the staff. Ball-faced hollow punch with opening just large enough to slip over the hairspring shoulder of the staff.

lathe and cutting it down very slightly with a cutting graver. Be sure the graver is sharp and the lathe is spinning at a fast speed. By reducing the size of the shank a little and trying the roller, your judgement will tell you when the staff is small enough that the roller can be driven on without injury.

Should the roller table drop all the way down to the shoulder without becoming tight, it is too large and must be corrected. A very quick and effective method for doing this is to place the roller table down in your stake on a flat ended stump. Place a three cornered punch in the center of the roller, and give it a few light taps. Your staking tool has a three or four cornered punch made especially for this operation. This does the roller table no real harm, if done carefully, but it does raise three burrs which create enough friction to hold the table firmly in place of the staff. As these burrs are inside the hole of the roller, they cannot be seen. But to strike too hard a blow here will ruin the roller. Caution is the watch word.

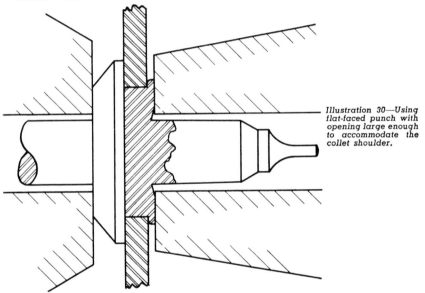

Illustration 30—Using flat-faced punch with opening large enough to accommodate the collet shoulder.

It is well to bear in mind that the fittings or rather the corrections outlined in the preceding paragraphs are seldom necessary if you use genuine material. That is, material made by the manufacturer who makes the watch, especially for the particular watch in question. For that reason, all good workmen buy and use only genuine material whenever and wherever possible.

Exceptions, of course, will be found where even the genuine material will not fit correctly, making certain changes necessary. That is because the watch has been improperly repaired or some piece of imitation material has been fitted previously. Therefore, you should resolve now to do every job as nearly perfect as possible. It saves trouble for yourself and others, and what is more important, it saves your time. In watchmaking, time is money.

LESSON EIGHT

Staking in the Staff

We have now reached the place in staff fitting where we know the staff will fit all the essential parts except the jewels. For the experienced workman, NOW is the proper time to fit the jewels. For a beginner, however, slightly different methods are suggested.

Before attempting to stake the staff into the balance, study the preceding series of illustrations carefully. Be certain that you know just which part of the watch and just which punch each illustration represents. (See illustrations 28, 29 and 30) They are almost a lesson in themselves.

Place your stake in position to use both hands conveniently. Select a hole in the die of the stake that will just accommodate the shank of the staff, with just enough tolerance to permit freedom. Center this hole with your "center" punch — the long punch with the sharp point — and lock the die in that position by tightening the disc on the back of the stake.

Drop the shank of the staff in this hole and place the balance over it in the correct position.

If the balance does not drop down all the way on its hub, select a flat faced hollow punch with opening just large enough to fit over the staff hub. With this punch gently press balance arm down on hub firmly. See that it is resting squarely on the hub of the staff.

If neither the balance wheel nor the staff have been mishandled, the staff should now fit fairly tight. But it is not tight enough.

We now temporarily abandon the flat faced punch and select a ball faced hollow punch with an opening just large enough to slip over the hairspring shoulder of the staff.

Before continuing with this operation, study well the illustrations shown. This enlarged view will help you visualize the job you are doing.

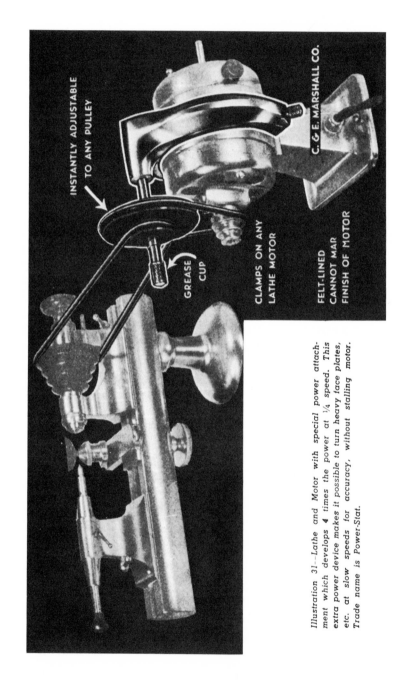

Illustration 31—Lathe and Motor with special power attachment which develops 4 times the power at ¼ speed. This extra power device makes it possible to turn heavy face plates, etc. at slow speeds for accuracy, without stalling motor. Trade name is Power-Stat.

Place this round faced punch in the stake and bring it down until it is resting on the staff. You are now ready to begin staking the staff. Use a fiber faced mallet so as not to harm the end of the punch. Tap the punch lightly a few times. This ball faced punch has a tendency to spread the hub. If the balance arm did not fit snugly on the staff, several strokes may be necessary to tighten.

This is a job that requires utmost caution. A wrong stroke or one stroke too many or too hard may cause serious damage to the staff or the balance arm.

Observe, too, that what you want to do here is to spread the shoulder just enough to hold the staff firmly. Therefore, your strokes must not be too hard. They should be comparatively light, quick bradding type of strokes rather than a "driving" type.

When the wheel no longer jumps around as the punch is struck, it is getting tight. Now switch to a flat faced punch with an opening just large enough to accommodate the collet shoulder. The opening in this punch should be approximately the same size as that of the

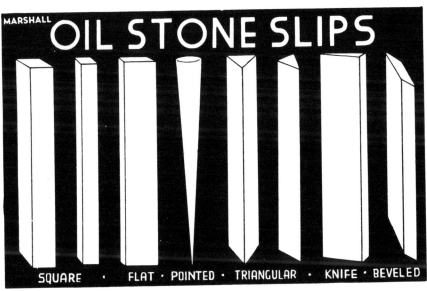

Illustrations 32 to 37—Oil stones are used for polishing pivots, finishing small machine parts, etc. Some of the well-known stones are Arkansas, India, Jasper, Carborundum, Bell Metal, Boxwood, Scotch Stone. They should be kept perfectly clean for best results. Oil stones are apt to wear hollow, and it is necessary to smooth them. For this purpose, take coarse emery and water upon a slate or marble slab, and with a circular motion grind the oil stone. Another very good way is to nail a piece of coarse emery paper upon a board, and grind the stone the same way as before.

ball faced punch first used. Use it in the same manner to complete the tightening of the staff. This is all shown clearly in the series of illustrations above.

To make certain that you get the staff just as tight as necessary, but no tighter, remove the wheel from the stake and test the staff occasionally.

This may be done by catching the shank of the staff in a pair of smooth-jawed flat-nose pliers and holding while you turn the balance with the fingers.

If the staff turns in the pliers rather than in the balance, it is probably tight enough. This operation requires some thought. It must not be too tight; it must not be too loose. So do not put too much pressure on the pliers or the wheel.

Illustration 38 — Mounted Jasper Slips. Jasper stones reduce and polish by one operation without the aid of any other substance. These pictures are about 2/3 size.

In performing the operation outlined above, be sure to hold the balance in the thumb and fingers of the left hand. Grasp it firmly at each end of the balance arm, but do not hold it tightly enough to injure the balance or get it out of true either in the round or the flat. But it should be tight enough to stand being trued and handled without moving in the balance arm.

If you have done the job correctly thus far, there should be very little truing to do.

Technique of Fitting Jewels to Pivots

The staff being fitted, the balance may now be handled without fear of having it flip out of the tweezers and away. That, too, is another thing you must learn by experience — just how tight to hold a piece of material to do with it as you wish, and yet not tight enough to cause it to flip from the tweezers. A good rule to follow is to hold it just as lightly as possible not to drop it.

You will find as you gradually go along and become more familiar with your tools and your eyes and muscles become properly coordinated, that these things gradually come to you. You will learn how much pressure is "too much", and how much it "too little". That is why it is suggested that you do these operations over and over again. Get more watch movements and study each one. Go over each just as you did the first. Repair it until you can almost do the entire job with your eyes closed. It never gets boring because each operation is new, each one teaches you something you have not had before. You must learn by doing. There is no other way.

Now take up the staff where we left off in the preceding lesson. For the sake of this lesson, we are going to assume that the pivots do not fit the jewels, and no other jewels are available. There will be further instructions on this in a later lesson, but for the moment we are going to fit jewels.

Remove both the top and bottom balance hole jewels. In the Hamilton on which we are now working, these jewels are interchangeable. In certain other well known makes; the top and bottom jewels are not interchangeable. For that reason it is well to train yourself from the beginning to keep them separated at all times. Learn to know which should be cock and which should be foot, if they are different.

In one respect they should always be the same — that is in pivot hole size. The only accurate way to determine this is with a jewel hole gauge. But for the moment we may make a test with the jewel itself that will suffice.

Push the staff into the block of pith. With the tweezers place the top or cock balance jewel over the top of the pivot. The pivot should come through the hole enough that the end can be seen and felt above the top of the jewel setting. If the jewel drops down to the pivot shoulder, the jewel is obviously too large and should be exchanged for a smaller one.

Changing the jewel for a different size is simple. Get your Ham-

Illustration 39—Metal burnisher for grinding and polishing pivots. The surface is just rough enough to do the job, yet leave the pivot perfectly polished.

ilton chart and select a jewel which is one-half number larger hole size than the staff. That is, if the staff has a pivot size 11, jewel should be hole size 11½.

Learn to read your chart. It gives the pivot size of each staff and the hole size of each jewel. In reordering, always specify sizes wanted and always put them in the correct bottle. It will save a lot of time.

There will be times, however, when you will not have the jewel you need. The staff will be so large that it will not go through the jewel. Then you must know what to do.

Begin by chucking the staff into the lathe. (See illustration 31) Do not draw it tight until you have spun it true. By studying the picture of the lathe you will see how this is easily done by raising the T rest and placing a piece of hard pegwood against the shank of the staff and spinning the lathe until the pivot is perfectly true. Then tighten the chuck.

If the pivot is very much too large, you must use an oil stone slip to reduce it. (See illustrations 32 to 37)

You do not use the T rest with the oil stone slip. Instead, you hold the stone between the thumb and fingers of both hands. Place the edge underneath the pivot, and hold the stone in such a manner that you actually grind the pivot evenly from end to shoulders as the staff revolves in the lathe.

Spin the staff at a moderate rate of speed.

Meanwhile, slowly move the stone back and forth in a smooth even stroke. All the while keep an eye loupe on the work so you can see that it is even — not being cut off to a needle-like point, or a ring cut around it. Remember: the pivot must retain complete uniformity.

After a few turns of the lathe, stop the work, use a piece of soft pegwood or pith to clean the pivot and try the jewel again to see if the pivot has been reduced to the proper size.

Illustration 40—Hard Arkansas oil stone. Mounted in wooden box.

You need not take the staff out of the lathe to do this. Instead, gently blow the breath on the end of the second finger of the right hand. Place that finger against the jewel. The moisture will cause the jewel to adhere to the finger until it can be lifted to the end of the staff. Slip it over the pivot. If the pivot is still large, repeat the operations until the pivot will go through the jewel, fitting rather snugly. The pivot is now ready for polishing.

Before going on, examine the pivot with a good eye loupe. You can now see how rough the pivot really is. With the naked eye it may look smooth, but with a strong loupe it looks like a large piece of unfinished steel — which is exactly what it is.

Now for the polishing. First use a good hard jasper slip. (See illustration 38) Use it exactly as you used the oil stone slip. The jasper being hard and fine-grained will reduce the size just enough to permit freedom of the pivot which, you will remember, we stopped grinding when it would just come through the jewel. The jasper slip will take off the roughness left by the coarse oil stone.

Now comes the burnisher. This is a specially prepared piece of steel (See illustration 39) that is ideal for smoothing up rough places left from the previous operations. Used in the same manner as the jasper slip, it gives the steel pivot a hard, smooth finish. (See lesson 10 for instructions on preparing the burnisher.)

The pivot now looks to be in perfect condition. It should be bright, evenly finished, and of uniform size. But the job is not yet finished. The finishing comes next.

Select a good piece of hard pegwood and use a very sharp knife to trim approximately one inch of the end to a square. Make it smooth and uniform with edges at perfect right angles. Dampen this square end and insert it in a bottle of good grade Diamantine. (This may be had from your supply house.) When the end is thoroughly charged with this powder, knock off the surplus and rub the stick gently over the neck of the bottle, pressing the powder well into the wood.

Let it dry for a few minutes, then proceed to polish the pivot just as you did with the oilstone and jasper. As you begin polishing you will notice that the pivot begins ot brighten like a mirror. Conversely

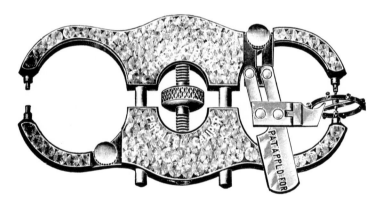

Illustration 41—*Truing calipers. Fitted with new parallel guide and index. Being parallel, the staff is always in perfect alignment.*

the pegwood will turn black at first. After several revolutions of the lathe, the pegwood will become less black as it is moved to a new place. This means the pivot is becoming nearer a mirror finish.

Examine it now with the strong eye loupe. It should be smooth, bright, and eye perfect. If so, you are now ready to reverse the staff in your lathe and proceed to repeat the above operations on the other pivot. It is well to use the same jewel as a gauge. By doing this, you can get both pivots the same size. This, too, is essential in accurate timekeeping. We are interested in no other kind.

Before removing the staff from the lathe, it is well to hold a flat side of the jasper slip directly against the end of the pivot. As you do this, revolve the lathe slowly. Do not polish the end of the pivot. Leave the end just as flat as you can get it. If the jasper is held at an angle, the pivot will have a round end. Be certain to hold it perfectly flat.

Some very good workmen round the ends of the pivots and seem to get satisfactory results. On the whole, however, you will always get better results with flat ends.

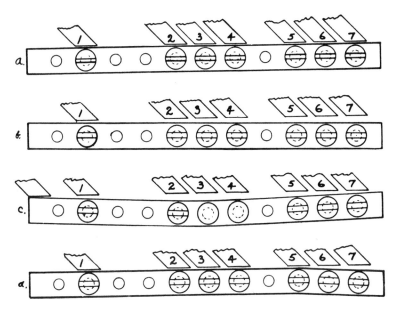

Illustrations 42 to 45—Sketches of balance index and balance rim.

The Burnisher--Putting it in Shape

The burnisher as the watchmakers know it, cannot be bought. True, you must buy the unfinished product and then finish it to suit yourself. Considerable skill is needed in an operation of this kind.

Get an unfinished burnisher (See illustration 39) from your supply house. In its present condition it is almost useless, therefore we must make it usable; first, secure a fairly fast cutting oilstone. (See illustration 40) Lay the burnisher flat on the oilstone and grasp it firmly with the thumb and tips of fingers of the right hand in such manner that you can bring it back and forth across the oilstone in even, smooth, powerful strokes.

Repeat this operation until the high spots have been worked down and the entire surface is even. Do this to all four sides. Be certain to make the corners sharp. See that they are straight and even; that there are no broken edges. When this is done, finish it on all four sides with a slower, smoother cutting stone. The surface is now probably highly polished. If so, use a good emery stick or a piece of emery paper to put on the finishing touches.

Before using the emery, however, slightly round one corner of the burnisher. It should be shaped to fit snugly along side a conical pivot.

Now draw the emery paper directly across the burnisher. Do not pull the burnisher length-wise across it as you did the oil stone. Pull it directly across the burnishing surface. Do not rough up the surface. It must not grind or file the pivot. But take off the bright polish and leave it just rough enough that the lines of the emery may be seen with a strong eye loupe.

When the job is as nearly perfect as you can make it, select an inexpensive fountain pen barrel and remove the point and ink sac. Fill this opening with plaster-of-paris and insert the pointed end of the burnisher. See that it is set straight and low enough to get the cap on over it. Let it set until the plaster-of-paris dries. It is now ready for use.

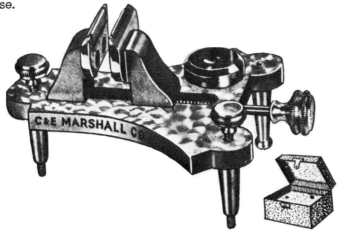

Illustration 46—Poising tool, with spirit level and agate jaws. Adjustable screw legs for leveling.

Easy Way of Truing Balance

The staff is now ready. Place the jewels back into the plates, see that they are clean, and oil them as instructed in a previous lesson. Place the balance on the plate and the cock in position over it. Tighten the cock screw and test the balance for complete freedom of action. When the end shake is correct, and the balance is completely free, you are ready to true the balance.

Too much stress cannot be put on the importance of truing the balance. A watch with an untrue balance cannot keep accurate time.

In this lesson, as in many others, we must learn to use a tool while we are learning to true the balance. The operations of the two are so interwoven that there is no other way to do it. It would seem to be far simpler to learn to operate the truing calipers and then learn to true the balance with them. But, alas, is cannot be done that way. The truing caliper (See illustration 41) is one of the most important tools you will be called upon to use. Learn it well.

Examine these calipers closely. There are many styles and makes. It is strongly urged that you get the ones shown here, as they are best suited for all work.

Before we begin working with the caliper, however, there is one important change to be made. The index arm is held with a thumb screw. See that it is placed on the caliper just as shown in illustration 41. Then remove the screw holding the indicator and turn the indicator over and replace it. After this is done, the point of the indicator will be pointing downward.

You will notice also that the parallel jaws are opened and closed by adjusting the screw in the center of the caliper. Work this back and forth a few times to get the feel of it. Clasp the caliper in the left hand with the indicator arm pointing down. Use the left thumb to work the index back and forth to change positions of the indicator arm. Before doing this, release the thumb screw holding index. Always when using the tool see that the index arm is just loose enough to work freely back and forth on the bottom arm. When you have finished with the caliper, tighten the thumb screw to hold index in place before laying it away.

You should now be familiar enough with the caliper to start using it. Keep it grasped in the left hand and use the thumb to open the jaws just wide enough to accommodate the staff of the balance we are going to true. Place the balance in bottom side up. Now tighten down until balance will no longer turn freely, but is just tight enough to have to be turned with the finger, and will stay wherever stopped.

We are now ready for truing. Some truing work can be done with the hand. However, I find that a better way is to use a good pair of tweezers with a not-too-fine point. If the balance is compensated — that is a cut balance such as the 16 size Hamilton we are now truing — begin first at the end of one arm. Let the indicator remain steadfast to the index arm, but adjust the position of indicator by moving the index arm back and forth as need be.

Place the indicator over one balance arm in such manner that it rests very lightly against the rim of the balance wheel. Hold the index in that position with the left thumb, and with the right thumb and fingers turn the wheel one half way around. By doing this, you discover which end is higher and which is lower. In correcting this, the arm must be raised or lowered by changing position at the staff. Never bend the arm between the end and the center.

Use a good eye loupe at all times when truing a balance. The object is to bring the ends of the arms to the exact same height. This is done by placing one point of the tweezers on top of the balance arm and one point underneath, and lifting gently upward or downward on the end of the arm. As the arm is somewhat elastic, you will have to move it somewhat more than the adjustment itself, as it will spring back when released. In a job of this kind, extreme care must be exercised at all times. Not much pressure is needed to spring a balance.

When the arms are parallel, observe the ends of the rim in relation to the arms. If they are up or down, they may be sprung back to position. Now place the indicator over the highest place in the entire rim and slowly turn the wheel. Note both the high and the low places. Wherever they may be, they must be brought to the exact same height. Usually it is necessary to adjust from both sides. The high side is too high, the low side too low. The true flat being somewhere in between. Thus you raise one a little and lower the other. (See illustrations 42 to 45)

After each operation, test the wheel again by placing the indicator on the rim at the high spot and turning the balance. When there is no longer a high spot or low place in the rim, it is true. Remove indicator by sliding the index back. Release the center screw just enough to permit the balance to twirl easily. Twirl it and notice how true it runs. If there is the slightest wobble, it is not yet true. With experienced watchmakers, several minutes is often required to true a balance. It will take you much longer at first. After you learn exactly what to do and how to do it, then try for speed.

When it is true in the flat, you must test it in the round. Begin this at the arm. Place the indicator along-side the rim as near the rim as possible. Hold the index in this exact position while you slowly turn the balance. If the indicator's relation to the rim changes at any point, there is where it is out. True one segment at a time. Then begin at the end of the other arm and true the other segment.

The above instructions on truing a balance in the round apply to all compensated balances. However, with the solid balances so much in use today, there is little you can do when a balance is out of true in the round. To offset this, it may be safely said that a solid balance properly handled will seldom get out in the round, and therefore will require little work of this kind. Moral: Be certain that you do not get a solid balance out of true in the round. You can save yourself a lot of grief this way. After you have fit a staff or two you will see what I mean.

If a balance persists in being untrue, look for the trouble elsewhere. It most likely is not sufficiently tight on the staff. If that is the case, remove the roller table in the usual way and proceed to tighten staff in the usual way.

When you encounter one that simply will not true — and you will encounter this kind — lay it aside and walk around the block. Perhaps drink a coke. The walk will relax you. When you take the balance up again, you will find it much easier to do. Remember, it was true once. And every day watchmakers are making good money because they know it can be trued, and they know how to do it.

Poising the Balance

The British Royal Air Force is generally credited with the discovery of the very annoying little people known as gremlins. Various war correspondents and Walt Disney have combined their talents to publicize these little gentlemen who cause so much trouble in this world.

Well, to the watchmaker, the gremlin is no new-found pest. He is an old standby, having been around for years. Often he has been called by other names — some of which are not printable. No doubt you have already discovered one or more about your work bench. When truing a balance, for instance, it is a gremlin who pulls it out each time you have it true. It is a gremlin that stops the watch just when you think it is in perfect working order. It is a gremlin that locks the hands after the job is finished. It is a gremlin that pushes the hairspring stud out each time you try to put it in place. They crawl in the pivot holes. They drink the oil. They wind small hairs around the escape wheel. In short, they do the thousand and one things that cause trouble that only a gremlin could cause.

But do not overlook one fact concerning the gremlin: When you have made the necessary corrections, that good gremlin — Mac — takes charge and sees that the watch performs as it should.

It is the gremlin, too, that swings around on a balance screw, keeping the watch out of poise. Occasionally he will change from one screw to another, so the same one is never heavy twice. All of this gremlin talk brings us to the lesson at hand — poising the balance. You may always expect gremlins here. If you fail to poise the balance, you are certain to have them.

You have the staff fitted to the balance, the jewels are fitted to the staff and the balance is true. Now for the poising.

In this lesson we learn the use of the Poising Tool. (See illustration 46) This tool is not nearly so complicated as the truing caliper which we had in the previous lesson. Its function is entirely different but no less important. A watch whose balance is not poised, WILL NOT KEEP TIME. It may make a good rate in one position, but in other positions it will run either fast or slow. So much so that the mean time will be far from accurate. For that reason, poising is one of the most important jobs to be done.

The poising tool as you see from illustration 46 has two parallel jaws. On the better tools these jaws are of polished agate. Agate gives a smooth, even space for the pivots to rest, causing as little friction as possible and offering as little space to accumulate dust as possible. The legs are adjustable to height. Your bench top should be level, the tool then may be levelled on the bench by adjusting the legs. Also most good poising tools have their own levels for this purpose.

On the right side of the tool is a thumb screw which opens and closes the parallel jaws to any desired position. This makes it ad-

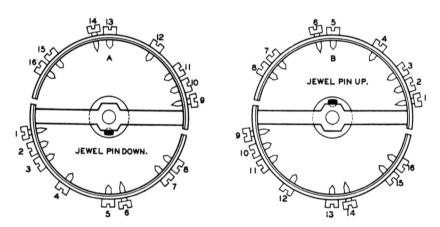

Illustrations 47, 48—Balance Wheels A and B illustrate the effect of counter-poise upon position error. In A and B the balance wheel is heavy at screw 5 and 13, the weight being sufficient to cause the balance to be held in the vertical position shown. If these two balances are placed in watches and tested in three positions, dial up, dial down and pendant up, the pendant up position will show a gain or loss depending upon the balance motion as follows: (A) in this condition and in the pendant up position the watch will gain in the short arcs and lose in the long arcs of motion. (B) in this condition and in the pendant up position the watch will gain in the long arcs and lose in the short arcs of motion. This gain or loss depending as it does on the "motion" of the balance, increases with counterpoise and decreases as the balance becomes more perfectly poised. The principle is described here to impress the necessity of a perfectly poised balance if accurate time is expected.

justable to any length staff. Before the staff is placed on it, it should be opened just enough so that the pivots rest on each jaw and the cone of the pivots do not touch the jaw.

Set this tool just to the left of your work plate. Place the parallel jaws just wide enough to rest the pivots on the agate edges. Have roller table facing you. That is, again work from the bottom side of the balance wheel. In taking it off the poising tool and putting it back, always maintain this position.

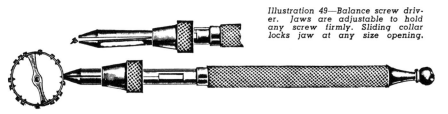

Illustration 49—Balance screw driver. Jaws are adjustable to hold any screw firmly. Sliding collar locks jaw at any size opening.

So far as results are concerned, it does not really matter which side you work from. The point is, to work from the same side at all times, thus avoiding time-killing errors.

Now take your balance and place it on the tool. Adjust the jaws to contact the pivots properly. Jaws of tool and pivots of staff must be clean and absolutely free of dust and oil. We release the wheel thus, and notice that it immediately begins turning. If the jaws of the tool are level, it will make only a turn or two in one direction. Then it starts rocking back and forth. Gradually the arcs become shorter and shorter. See that air currents do not strike it. Finally it stops swinging. The force of gravity has forced the heavy side down.

Notice now which balance screw is directly on top. This, of course, is the light screw. The heavy screw is diametrically opposite. This, then, is where the balance is out of poise. This may not be the only place. Perhaps it is just the heaviest one. (See illustrations 47 and 48)

Restoring Equilibrium of the Balance

There are a number of "do's" and "don'ts" in bringing a balance to poise. The word POISE, of course, means the quality of being balanced; to place or support in equilibrium. Hence a wheel out of poise is one out of balance or unbalanced. A watch will run with a wheel out of poise. It may, on occasion, keep time lying on its back — or dial up position. If so, with pendant up it will run slow; pendant down it will run fast. Pendant right and pendant left it will be similarly affected.

Adjusting a watch so it will keep the same rate in all these positions, is known as position timing. Better watches are stamped "adjusted to six positions". Basically, these six positions are as follows: Dial up; dial down; pendant up; pendant down; pendant right: pendant left. Properly poising the balance is the first step in achieving correct time in all positions.

If you make a watch keep accurate time in all these positions, you may be sure it will give you very little trouble.

Now, back to the wheel itself. We found that it had a heavy side and a light side; or rather, it has a heavy side OR a light side. We cannot tell which, because this total weight is relative to the entire mass of the balance and the strength of the hairspring. What to do?

If we take off weight on the heavy side, this lightens the entire balance causing the watch to run faster. If we add weight to the light side, this added weight will make the watch run slower. So it would seem the proper course is to add just as much to the light side as is taken away from the heavy side. If the wheel were perfectly poised before the staff was broken, then the above course would be the proper one. However, it is difficult to tell how much weight is removed at a given operation. Thereby hangs the trouble.

There are as many theories here as there are watchmakers. However, we are not dealing with theory in this series of lessons. We are trying to be practical. Obviously the best thing to do is try the watch and see if the balance needs to be heavier, lighter, or approximately the same weight as a whole. This is easy if you have a WATCH-MASTER timing machine — which you probably will not. And without such a machine, this takes up a lot of time.

With the timing machine at hand, you might proceed as follows: Make a small cross scratch on the end of the timing screw that stopped on top. Remember the marked screw is the light one. Now put on

Illustration 50—Balance screw undercutters; 7 prong set. For timing and poising balance wheels. Place screw in hollow of cutter and turn with screw driver.

the hairspring just as if the watch were finished. Then place the watch on the WATCHMASTER — described in detail in a later lesson — and find just what it does in each position. Thus you may determine if weight should be added or removed. If it makes a perfect rate in the flat position, for example, you know the total weight is approximately correct. Therefore we should add as much weight to the light side as is removed from the heavy side.

Keep the above paragraph in mind. You will see how valuable it is a little later.

If we do not have the use of a timing machine of any kind, we must learn to do it the hard way. In doing things the hard way, it is well to strive to make that way as easy as is humanly possible.

Let us again take up the balance where we first discovered we had a light and a heavy side. Because it is far easier to add a given amount of weight to a balance than to remove a given amount, the following method is suggested.

The force of gravity has brought the heavy screw to rest on the bottom. We tip the wheel lightly with the tweezer point and let it rock back and forth until it comes to rest again. Again it is the same screw that is on the bottom — or rather since we can only see the top of the balance, the same screw is pointing heavenward. We know this is directly opposite the heavy screw, which we want to lighten until complete equilibrium is reached.

Be positive you have the heavy screw spotted before proceeding to lighten it.

If you have been wondering how we are going to lighten this heavy screw and have been thinking of a file, get it off your mind. Always remember, a good watchmaker never uses a file on a watch. True, you will find a lot of watches and balances that have been filed. Some have been ruined that way. So the statement is worth repeating: A good watchmaker never files a balance.

Here is what you should do.

Select a good balance screw holder. (See illustration 49) This tool comes in eight sizes and one size will be certain to fit the watch

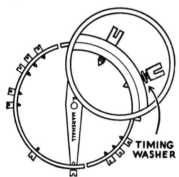

TIMING WASHER

Illustration 51—Balance timing washers. USE OF WASHERS: If the watch accelerates its rate, bring it to time by means of washers under the heads of the screws, if the balance is not provided with mean-time screws. These watches are cut out of brass or gold plate rolled down to as thin as 1/1000 of an inch. Place pairs of these washers under opposite screws, usually the screws at the extremeties of the balance arms. A little experience will soon guide you to correct given errors; also you can always present the watch with the regulator in the center, something which many customers look at.

we are now working with. Clamp this holder on the heavy screw — holding the balance rim near the screw so we do not force it out of true — gently screw the heavy screw out of the balance. Be certain to tighten the screw holder sufficiently to remove the screw without marring its contours.

To make the screw lighter, we learn to use another tool — the undercutter. (See illustration 50) There are several types of under-cutters available. The one shown here is probably as good as can be had today.

Examine these cutters with your eye loupe and you will find a hollow pipe with two cutting edges. You will readily see that when the balance screw is inserted and turned, these edges shave off just a small shaving of metal next to the screw threads. Remember, a little goes a long way here. If you get a good cutting, it is well to use only a very little pressure. Make from six to ten turns of the screw holder.

Then insert the screw and try the balance on the poising tool again.

Repeat this operation if necessary until the heavy side is equal to the opposite one. When these sides are equal, there may now be another heavy side. It would have shown up before, except for the fact the first screw was heavier. Repeat the operation again and again, being careful not to cut the screws too much. If we get them too light then the opposite screw becomes the heavy one. In this case we are making the balance lighter without actually accomplishing anything.

When it is so poised that it will stay in any position in which it is stopped, without rocking, and when a twirl will cause it to turn several rounds and come to a stop without rocking and without doing so in the same place twice, it is in poise. Bear in mind that a magnetized wheel will not come to poise. Perhaps the pull of the magnetic pole is too great on it. Remove the magnetism and it may be in poise.

A wheel properly poised thus shows no outward sign of having been worked on at all. There should be no filed screws or flat sides. No scratches or blemishes. That is a factory job.

The Secret of "Timing" a Watch

It will not be easy to learn poising. It sounds simple. It is simple. That is why it is so difficult.

Before we proceed with our original balance, it is well to remember that we poised the wheel by taking off weight. We did this to expedite the work. Now it may be necessary to add weight to bring the balance back to normal. This can be easily accomplished by using timing washers. These are small washers which may be had from your supply house. They are charted according to size and weight and the approximate number of seconds they will effect a watch within a 24 hour period.

On a compensated balance, washers will effect the watch more if placed near the compensations than if placed nearer the end of the arm. To place them on a watch, select two from the same bottle as they are the same size and weight. Place them on the balance by removing a balance screw, placing the washer on it and placing the screw back in the balance. (See illustration 51) Now place the other washer on the diametrically opposite screw. Thus you add weight without changing the poise.

Give it a final test. See that it is as nearly perfect as possible. Take another quick glance at the rim to see if you have gotten it out of true in poising it. This sometimes happens. There are certain balances that are so soft that poising will get them out of true, and truing will get them out of poise. They require special care.

The Hamilton with which we are still working is not one of that kind. Therefore, we are ready to proceed. Now we have a balance wheel with the roller table attached. Test the roller jewel to make certain it is tight. If so, locate the mark on the balance rim indicating

the position of the hairspring stud. Select a flat faced stump for the
stake. Set balance on stump. See that safety roller rests securely on
face of stump. Place the hairspring on the balance and with a hollow ended punch, just large enough to accommodate the staff, gently
push the spring collet down until it rests on the balance arm. Make
sure it is flat. Also, the hairspring should be flat except for the overcoil. All spaces between coils should be equal. The study of the

Effect of Meantime Screws		
Size	No. of Turns of Meantime Screws	Seconds per Hour
18–16	1 Full Turn on 4 Screws	6
18–16	½ Turn on 4 Screws	3
18–16	¼ Turn on 4 Screws	1.5
18–16	¼ Turn on 2 Screws	.75
12	1 Full Turn on 4 Screws	4
12	½ Turn on 4 Screws	2
12	¼ Turn on 4 Screws	1
12	¼ Turn on 2 Screws	.5
6/0	1 Full Turn on 4 Screws	10
6/0	½ Turn on 4 Screws	5
6/0	¼ Turn on 4 Screws	2.5
6/0	¼ Turn on 2 Screws	1.25
18/0	1 Full Turn on 4 Screws	10
18/0	½ Turn on 4 Screws	5
18/0	¼ Turn on 4 Screws	2.5
18/0	¼ Turn on 2 Screws	1.25

Illustration 52—Effect of meantime screws.

hairspring will come in a later chapter. But bear in mind that it is the most important part of the watch.

The balance is now ready to place on the cock.

Perhaps by this time you have learned how to handle your tweezers almost any way. If not, begin practising. Here is a pointer. The balance cock is lying before you, bottom up. Take the tweezers in the right hand, turn the hand over to the right until the bottom point

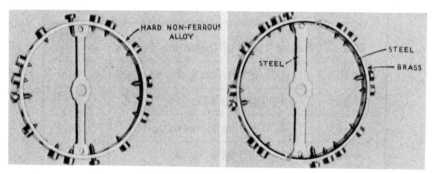

Illustration 53 — Monometallic balance wheel (not cut).   Illustration 54—Bi-metallic balance wheel.

of the tweezer is on top. Now place it on the balance cock. Lift it off the bench and turn the hand back to the left to a normal position. The balance wheel is now dangling from the cock with only the hairspring holding it.

Thus we prepare to place it in the watch. We know that in order for the watch to run, the roller jewel must come into the fork correctly. In short, it must come into the jewel slot smoothly. This is done by turning your hand until the roller jewel is on the same side of the line of centers as the fork slot. That is, if the fork is resting against the left banking pin, then the roller jewel must be to the left of the line of centers — this line of centers being referred to is from escape wheel pivot directly through fork pivot to balance pivot. First let the balance wheel drop into position. Gently ease down on the balance cock until you can let it come to rest on the plate. You can now tell if the roller jewel is coming into the fork properly. If not, take the balance assembly up and try it again.

A little practice will show you just which wrist movements are necessary to accomplish this. When the roller jewel is right, let the cock come to rest and see that it goes into its place with the balance staff remaining free. This, too, will require a little practice. You may now place the cock screw in position and tighten it down only after the balance is running freely.

If your work has been done well, the watch is now running and taking good motion. By "good motion" is meant the balance makes an arc of 360 degrees or more with each stroke.

For the moment let's assume that the motion is good and we now have only to regulate the watch. With the Watchmaster this regulating in position is a simple matter. Since you do not have a machine, we must proceed with a slower method.

Place the dial and hands in position. Have on or near your bench a regulator. Here the term "regulator" refers to a watch or clock used for purposes of time comparison. It must be an excellent time piece

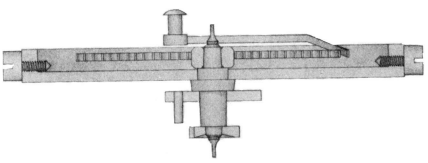

Illustration 55—The Breguet hairspring is exactly like the flat except for the over-coil, which is formed of approximately two-thirds of the outside coil.

and you must have confidence in it. Now set the watch to the correct time. Place the second hand right with your "regulator" to the second. There are many ways of doing this. Perhaps the safest is to use a very small long bristled, soft brush to hold against the balance wheel until the regulator second hand comes to the exact second at which you stopped the watch you are repairing. At that second, release the balance wheel and see that the two second hands run in unison.

Before doing this, of course, it is necessary to see that the hairspring stud is in the correct position. The spring should be flat, true in the round, and the overcoil should come directly between the regulator pins. Not pressing against either one of them. The pins should be straight and just wide enough apart to permit the spring to rest between them freely, and no more. They MUST not be so close as to pinch the spring. They must not be so wide as to permit the spring to play back and forth too much. All these things will follow in succeeding lessons.

Right now we are ready with our watch to proceed with position adjusting. Provided everything is working smoothly. The watch should be wound one turn of the ratchet wheel and placed pendant up. When it has run a given period — say four hours — check the number

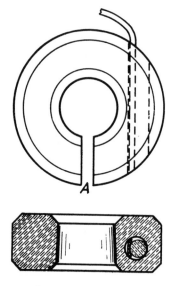

Illustrations 56, 57—Hairspring collet. First determine which way the
pin goes into the collet. The pin
is slightly tapered. Use the point
of a very fine needle to push the
pin out. Then take the spring out
of the collet.

of seconds gained or lost. With the spring wound only one turn, you will get the shortest vibration of the balance.

After four hours the rate of loss or gain is written down. The watch is wound one half turn and is placed pendant down. After four more hours, the rate is again noted.

Now wind the mainspring up so as to get the longest possible vibrations. Test it in four hour periods just as before.

Refer to your figures to determine the corrections to be made. For example, let us assume that the first position rate was 4 seconds slow (—4). In the second position it lost six seconds (—10). In the third position it gained five seconds, giving us (—5). Thus the mean variations of the two positions with short vibrations is represented by (—5), and the long vibrations by (plus 5).

As each trial was for four hours or one-sixth of 24 hours, to obtain one 24 hour period variation we multiply by six. Thus 6 x 5 equal —30, which added to plus 30 equals 60. Therefore the short arcs are one minute slow in 24 hours.

If the watch gains or loses in both the short and long arcs, then subtract one total from the other to get the mean daily rate.

We now know that the watch is fast, or slow. We know which and how much. If the wheel is perfectly poised, the variations must be caused by the hairspring being incorrect in the circle. First, however, check the regulator pins to see that they are neither too wide nor too close. See that the spring is leveled and circuled. See that escapement is correct at every point. If these things are all as they should be — and the jewels and pivots are correct — the correction may be made by changing the overcoil.

Generally speaking, make the overcoil flatter to speed the short arcs, and by making the overcoil a little shorter by taking some of it back into the body of the spring, the long arcs are made shorter. After every correction, make certain that when the balance is inert, with roller jewel resting in the line of centers, the hairspring is perfectly centered around the staff. That is to say, the collet must be directly in the center of the coils, with each coil an equal distance to each other coil.

That kind of operation requires a lot of patience and practice. After you have changed the spring as you think it should be, wind, set, and time just as before. When the vibrations and the rate is the same when only partially wound and when fully wound, you will know the adjusting is correct. Then you may add weight or move meantime screws until the correct rate is achieved. (See illustration 52)

In the foregoing paragraphs you have been told how to make certain corrections; others were mentioned and you were told they should be corrected, but as yet you do not know how to correct them.

That is what this series of lessons is designed to do— show you how to locate trouble — then show you how to correct it. You probably have not yet reached the latter stage. Even when you see the trouble now, many times you would not know what to do about it.

Therefore, let me urge you to read these lessons over and over again. Each time you will find some point overlooked the other times.

Actually do the work as you go along. Do not try to do the work very fast. Learn first to do it and do it right. Only by doing the same job over and over hundreds of times can you become proficient. Experience is the main thing you need now.

Illustration 58—New Swiss Hairspring system. Merely measure the diameter of balance with gauge as shown in illustration. Look on chart and opposite that diameter will be found the number of the box containing the proper hairspring. This system is just as easy as it sounds. Saves you time and trouble of measuring, calculating, classifying, etc.

Hairsprings—How to Work on Them

This lesson and the ones immediately following deal with the hairspring. You should know by now that it is one of the most important parts of the watch. Also perhaps the most delicate. To treat it completely would fill, by itself, a large book. Here it is not, therefore, our purpose to take up everything that might be discussed about the hairspring. Rather, it is our purpose to give you a sound basic knowledge of the spring and the part it plays. If the study of the hairspring intrigues you and you want more technical knowledge to go with your experience, then we have succeeded in part. The rest is up to you.

First, by way of explanation, there are two basic types of hairsprings: Breguet, and flat. The flat spring is so called because of its construction — which is just what the name implies, flat. It differs from the Breguet only in shape. That is, the Breguet has an overcoil. The final coil is turned up and over the body of the spring, forming what is known as an overcoil. Also, it is a Breguet spring — pronounced Brig-Gay — in honor of the French Watchmaker who first developed it.

The flat spring is not so much in use today as it once was. But many watches still use it. Observe the spring closely with your eye loupe and you will find that it is a very fine piece of spring steel which starts out from a central point — the collet— and makes a series of symmetrical turns until it reaches a given point where the stud is attached. Each coil is exactly like the other only larger in circumference. Being of fine spring steel, it is naturally subject to all the idiosyncrasies of any fine spring steel, such as rust, magnetism, and the like.

The Hamilton Watch Company was one of the leaders in developing a special balance wheel and hairspring that is both non-magnetic and rust resisting. (See illustrations 53 and 54) Watches equipped with these new balances have been found much more practical for use in the vicinity of magnetic fields than the old type. They do not magnetize. They are not affected by changes in temperature. Being rust resistant, they make the watch much more sturdy and reliable under all conditions. Not being affected by temperature changes, there is

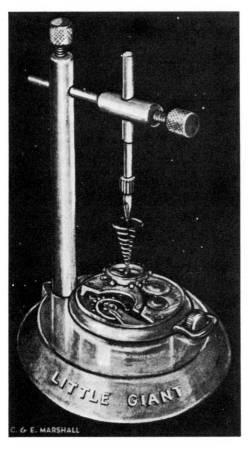

Illustration 59—Vibrating Tool. A complete precision instrument used in obtaining the correct beat of a balance wheel, or what is commonly termed "Hairspring Vibrating". The Master Balance is vibrated and timed to the standard, normal train — 18,000 beats per hour. Place the balance to be vibrated above the Master Balance (see illustration). Let rest slightly on the glass. Let the machine go. If the timing loses, shorten the hairspring. When it gains lengthen the hairspring. When the two balances are going well together for about 60 oscillations, make a point at the hairspring with a small file Stud by placing that point between the index pins.

no need for the compensated balance, therefore the new balances are solid.

All these characteristics are due to fairly recent discoveries in metals and their combinations from which the balances and springs are made. Hamilton uses the trade name of Elinvar to designate this special metal differing from steel in both composition and characteristics. Its reactions are negative under temperature changes and in or

HAIRSPRINGS—HOW TO WORK ON THEM 85

near magnetic fields. Since neither the spring nor the balance wheel
contracts nor expands with heat and cold, it maintains its poise and
even time-keeping qualities at all times.

You will notice that the Breguet hairspring is exactly like the flat
except for the overcoil. (See illustration 55) This overcoil is formed of
approximately two-thirds of the outside coil. At a given point it is

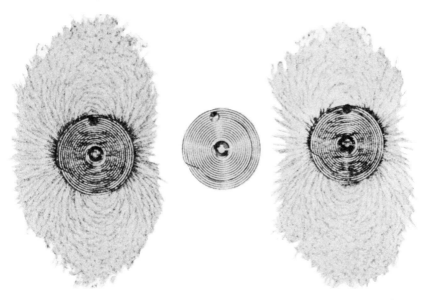

*Illustrations 60, 61, 62—Magnetism is a frequent cause of trouble to a watchmaker
because little is known about it. To understand everything about a magnetized
watch requires a knowledge of electricity.*

twisted slightly upward, then a short space further out it is turned
downward again. At this point it is turned in over the body of the
spring a distance of four coils. At that point it is again turned outward
and follows the curvature of the fourth coil around until the stud is
reached.

On different watches the overcoil is different. Each watch has its
own particular type of overcoil. On each watch of one model, however, the overcoil is always the same. This makes changing of hairsprings a simple matter.

Before proceeding, take your eye loupe and note carefully the
construction of the spring before you. Compare it with the picture

(illustration 55) and form a lasting mental image of the spring. Make it so vivid that you can close your eyes and see the entire outline of the spring within your mind. Note that the inside end is pinned in the collet. A small brass pin is used. Also the outside end is pinned to the stud in the same manner. Here, too, a small brass pin is used.

At first these pins look so delicate that you will think no one could pin and unpin them. But that is just what you are going to learn to do. In actually doing watch repairing, you will not likely have a lot of this kind of work to do. But doing it is excellent training. Furthermore, it will give you the "know how" so essential to any job. But when you do have to do a job of this kind you want to know how to proceed.

First determine which way the pin goes into the collet. The pin itself is slightly tapered. Use the point of a very fine needle to push the pin out. Take the spring out of the collet. Now put it back. Re-pin it. (See illustrations 56 and 57)

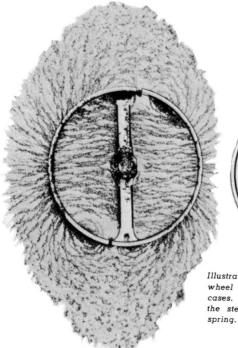

Illustrations 63, 64—A magnetized balance wheel gives most of the trouble in these cases. But magnetism might find its way to the stem, crown wheel or even the mainspring.

For experience, get a complete new pin. It will be somewhat longer than the one that came out. Place the spring in the collet and then insert the point of the new pin. Push it through until it becomes tight. Now use a small pair of tweezers or pliers to grasp the end that comes through and pull it through as far as possible. When it is quite tight and the spring is also tight in the collet, clip off the remaining ends flush with the collet, and level and circle the spring.

Caution: the inside coil must be round, flat, and must not touch the next coil or the collet at any place.

Repeat the above performance with the stud. Learn to pin it in such manner that very little leveling will be necessary when it is pinned. In doing this you are gaining invaluable experience in doing a delicate job. Do not despair if you fail a few times. If you ruin a few springs, get more and repeat until you can do the job correctly. Every beginner ruins springs, pins, and temper.

There will be times when you are boiling inside. Keep it inside. When you can stand it no longer, relax. Smoke. Walk around. After five minutes, come back and see how easy it is to do that vexing job now.

You will find as you go along from this to other watches that all Breguet hairsprings do not follow the outline given here. Each manufacturer has his own ideas about how a hairspring should be shaped. All watches by one factory will not use the same type overcoil. However, all watches by one factory bearing the same model number do have interchangeable parts throughout.

Hamilton hairsprings come in different strengths. The approximate strength is determined by the number of screws in the balance wheel.

So far in this lesson we have studied the hairspring to learn something of its make up and its reactions. As yet we have learned very little about it in actual practice. Before going into the actual work, however, we must first learn something about why it does what it does. That, remember, is important in anything. If we are really to know it, we must know why it does a given thing. Then we must know how it does it. Then we must know when it will do it. After you have learned these three essentials, there remains the knowing how to make it do it. That is the goal we are after.

The Train—"Beats per Hour"

We have not yet taken up the study of the train except to clean and assemble it. With watches standardized as they are today, you will not have to learn as much about the train as workmen once had to know. But you must be familiar with its functions — even if you don't know why it does certain things.

The circumference of any hairspring must be a given size in relation to the balance wheel and balance cock. That statement at this moment probably means nothing to you. But keep it in mind. Also a hairspring must be a given strength in relation to the weight of the balance wheel complete. We must learn how to determine the strength of spring for each wheel. It is not done with scales. The strength of the spring is determined by the weight of the wheel plus the speed of the train. To understand this we must give some thought to the train itself.

The Hamilton we are experimenting with has what is known as an 18,000 train. That is to say, the balance wheel makes 18,000 beats — or strokes — per hour. The large majority of watches now in use, has this train. Yet from time to time you will encounter other trains. Some as fast as 22,000 beats per hour; some as slow as 16,200 beats per hour. Both fast and slow trains are so scarce and are now being used so little that we shall confine this lesson to the standard 18,000 train.

At one time a thorough knowledge of the train gearing was absolutely essential. You had to understand the method of counting the wheel teeth and the pinion teeth and their proper divisions in order that injured wheels or pinions might be replaced. Mass production, however, forced standardization of watches to such an extent that we can discuss this matter lightly. If you care to go deeper into the subject, you may find many good books that go into complete details.

Today if you wish to know the train speed of any unusual watch, place it on any good Watchmaster rate recorder and in just 30 seconds you will know its speed. Any train wheel may be replaced by model and size, so you need not know the number of teeth or anything else to obtain the correct part.

Here at present we are concerned only with the 16 size Hamilton which we know has an 18,000 train. To reduce these figures to something more easily comprehended, and to show another method of determining the train speed, let us see how we arrive at 18,000. One beat

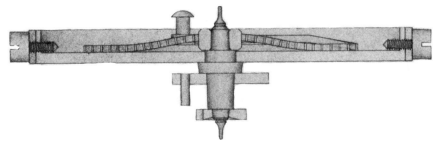

Illustration 65—Showing how magnetism sometimes affects hairsprings.

consists of one stroke of the balance wheel. To put it another way, one beat is one unlocking of the escapement. This is the passing of the escape tooth from resting on one pallet stone to the other. One stroke of the fork from one banking pin to the other.

Thus if you remove the balance and move the fork back and forth until it has unlocked the escapement five times, you will find that the second hand has moved exactly one second. The number of beats per second, five, times the number of seconds per minute. sixty, gives you 300 beats per minute. Three hundred beats per minute times the number of minutes per hour, sixty, gives you 18,000. Thus we find that an 18,000 train actually makes just five beats or strokes per second. The above figures are essential in vibrating a hairspring.

Best Way to Vibrate the Hairspring

Before going further, perhaps you should know the meaning of the term "to vibrate a hairspring". It means to get a spring just strong enough and just long enough to vibrate the balance exactly five times per second. Sounds easy. Before attempting to do it, however, do a little experimenting. Take the balance off the cock and catch the spring with your hairspring tweezers just back of the stud as near as possible to the position of the regulator pins when balance is in place on the cock. Remember, hairsprings are always vibrated from the position of the regulator pins rather than the position of the stud.

As you will not likely have the use of a vibrating tool, select a pocket watch with a second hand. Be sure the watch is keeping reasonably accurate time. Lay it on the bench before you, so that the balance arm is in clear view as the watch vibrates — or runs.

Catch the spring approximately where the overcoil rests between the regulator pins. Hold the tweezers perpendicularly. Let the balance pivot come to rest gently on the surface of the plate of the pocket watch on the bench before you. Holding the balance so the pivot will just come to rest on the plate, the hairspring is in the shape of a cone.

Now use the left hand to clasp the balance wheel thus suspended, and turn it at least one half way around. Then release it sharply on the beat of the other watch; that is, try to get the balance, which you are holding with your tweezers, to swing exactly with the balance of the watch. By experimenting a little with this, you will soon get the knack of it. The two balances must be synchronized perfectly until the power begins waning on the one you are holding. If they are so synchronized, then your hairspring is approximately right. Of course, we knew this one was right all the time.

However, if you really want to go further into it now, get another spring or two, replace the original with the new, and vibrate it in the same manner. If the strength is different, you will have to hold it in another position to get the two balances to synchronize. That, then, is where the regulator pins should rest on the new hairspring, regardless of where it is. Of course, no doubt the overcoil would have to be changed also, as the exact position of the overcoil must be maintained regardless of the strength of the spring being used.

If you care to make this same test another way, try it by working in the same manner, but holding the balance over the watch crystal and counting the number of strokes or vibrations per minute. Since you can count only half the vibrations, focus your eyes at the turning point of the balance. Start it vibrating exactly on the minute. Count the strokes as the balance arm comes to rest and reverses. Since you are counting only one side of the balance arm, you are counting just half the vibrations. And since there should be 300 vibrations per minute, half of that would be 150. You are counting only every other vibration; therefore, you should count exactly 75. Then glance quickly at the second hand of the master watch. If just exactly thirty seconds have elapsed, you are approximately correct. If you count more than 75 during this period, the spring is too strong and should be caught nearer the outside end. If you do not count 75 in the 30 second period, then it is too weak and should be tried a little further in on the outside coil. The 30 second period is suggested, as one minute is too long for a balance to vibrate without added momentum. To add momentum will throw the vibrations out.

The above method is not quite so accurate as the first one suggested. Neither are as accurate as the use of a good vibrating tool. (See illustrations 58 and 59) This tool is self explanatory. The tweezer like clamp suspended above the balance, is for holding the hairspring to be vibrated. When it is clamped, a gentle shake will start the two balances vibrating in unison. If they remain synchronized, the vibrations are approximately correct. Make correction just as outlined above.

From the brief descriptions above, you may have the impression that vibrating hairsprings is quite simple. It is not hard but there is a certain knack you must acquire through practice. Great accuracy is necessary.

After you have vibrated the spring as nearly correct as possible, remember that where it is being held is where the regulator pins must rest. Therefore, we must allow enough additional end to reach the stud. Then pin the spring to the stud, level it both in the flat and in the round. Put the watch in beat again. Now set the watch with your regulator. Place the second hands exactly together and test it for one hour, two hour, or even longer periods in each position. Any variations in time must be accounted for in the usual manner.

The above instructions are given as experience exercises. Do them over and over. This is one of the finest exercise for the hands and eyes. Repeat the operations until you can do it perfectly. Then you will know you are getting somewhere.

Hairspring Leveling and Straightening

In the preceding lesson we have dealt briefly with the hairspring. However, we have dealt only with the Breguet spring. And with only one type of Breguet. There are many breguets and many flat springs still in use. It is impossible in a work of this kind to cover them fully.

The flat spring is found largely in Swiss watches. Also some American wrist watches. The flat spring is vibrated exactly as the Breguet. The difference being that, lacking an overcoil, extreme accuracy is not so essential. After the flat spring is vibrated approximately one fourth turn should be permitted to protrude through the stud after the spring has been pinned. This additional spring will permit necessary changes after the watch is put in test.

Before leaving, just a word about pinning springs. If a new pin is used, secure a good grade of stud pin which may be had from your supply house. Place the end of the spring in the stud of collet and push the small end of the pin into the stud with the spring. After you have pushed it through as far as you can, catch the other end with a pair of good tweezers or pliers and pull until the pin is tight. You will find that after you have pushed it as far as possible, it will still pull through. Now break or clip the ends off. Some stud pins break off evenly. Some have to be clipped. For this use a good cutting tweezer or plier. Clip the end close and see that it does not contact the coils of the spring.

After the stud is pinned, adjust the spring so that the outside coil rests between the regulator pins. It must rest squarely between them, pressing against neither when the balance is resting inert, with the roller jewel facing the line of centers between the banking pins.

The regulator should rest exactly in the center of the index.

Level the spring in the flat. See that the stud is neither too high nor too low in the cock. Now true it in the round. The spring should be so trued that the collet is exactly in the center of the spring as it rests on the balance staff. If you have difficulty truing the spring in the round — and you will — a very good method is to take it off the balance wheel and place the stud in the cock and tighten the stud screw just enough to hold the spring in place.

Turn the balance cock bottom side up and adjust the spring so the center of the collet rests directly over the center of the cock whole jewel. These centers can easily be determined with the eye loupe.

We are spending considerable time with the hairspring. It may seem foolish to you now. A few months from now you will realize how important it really was. It is impossible to take up every spring trouble and tell you how to correct it. Nor do I think it desirable to do so. Better learn how to make these corrections as you go along. Learn where the spring is out of true. Put it back exactly where it is out.

Occasionally you will drop a spring, or let it slip from your tweezers. At first you will think it is ruined. But many times it is only tangled. These tangles are easily taken out if you follow a few simple rules. The coils may be over or under each other. Try pulling the balance first one way then the other. This may or may not straighten it. If not, take a small steel wire and taper it to a fine point. Let is be three inches long. The larger part should be too large for any collet. The small end should be gradually tapered down small enough to accommodate the smallest collet. Anchor this wire in a lead or other heavy base to keep it secure on the bench.

When you have a tangled hairspring, first remove it from the balance if it is not already off. Then place the stud in the cock and remove the stud pin. Now place the spring over the steel anchor described above. Push the collet down until it is tight enough not to turn.

Now select a small pivot broach. Insert the point between the coils of the spring down near the collet, well below the beginning of the tangle. Run the broach around the coils of the spring, working outward at all times.

By doing this carefully you will work the tangles completely out of the spring, after which it may be replaced in the stud. If any coils are bent so they are closer on one side of the spring and wider on the other, locate the bent place and adjust it there. Be certain the spring is flat. If one side is high, it may well be due to an error within the first one-half turn from the collet. If so, there is the place it must be corrected. The first complete turn from the collet must be level and uniform in curvature. It must not touch the collet except where it is pinned. It must not be far enough away from the collet to throw the spring out of round.

These suggestions are of necessity brief and general. The purpose is to train your eyes to locate the errors and train your hands to correct them. If certain errors were shown in detail and their corrections illustrated with photographs, it would be of little help. You might never encounter those exact conditions.

We now have the spring in the watch. Everything is in readiness to test it. Of course the watch must be in beat. If the wheel is perfectly poised, and all pivots and jewels are correct, the rate should be the same in all positions.

If the spring is not flat and/or not true in the round, the rate will naturally vary in the different positions. So, if it varies, check the spring for "out" in the flat. Also for "out" in the round. Correct it. Occasionally a small change will make a big difference in the rate of a watch. Other times a large change in the spring will make only a small difference in the rate of the watch. That is just one of the uncertainties of watchmaking.

When the spring is perfect and the rate is the same in every position, then is time enough to begin regulation. By simple multiplication, you can compute the seconds per hour gained or lost, and know what the variation will be over a 24 hour period.

If the rate is fast, that means the spring is too short. If the gain is several minutes over a 24 hour period, the spring may be un-pinned and made just a little longer, and re-pinned a little nearer the end. If too slow, that means the spring is too long. If the loss is several minutes, the easier way to correct it is to pin the spring a little shorter.

Each of these changes will throw the watch out of beat.

A watch perfectly in beat — to be covered in detail in a following lesson — may best be explained to you as one in which the "tick" and the "tock" are of the exact same duration. Another way to explain it is this: — when the power is off the train, the roller jewel comes to rest exactly between the banking pins. Then when the watch is wound, the roller jewel will start its motion from the line of centers and will swing the same distance in each direction.

If you re-pin the spring to make the correction in time, the watch may be put in beat by the simple process of moving the spring collet on the staff until the roller jewel will come to rest along the line of centers. First determine which way the jewel should go to bring the watch back to beat. Then remove the balance assembly from the watch and insert the point of a sharp very small screwdriver blade in the slot of the hairspring collet. Move it gently in the desired direction to change the position of the roller jewel in relation to the hairspring stud.

With these corrections made, you are ready to test the watch in positions again. You must depend on the ear to tell you when the watch is in beat. Pocket watches may be heard very easily. Sometimes the smaller models are difficult to hear distinctly, in which case you may amplify the sound by placing the movement in a small material box and pressing the box against the ear. Also, experience is one of the best teachers here. With the proper training, the ear will be able to detect a slight variation in the beats of "tick" and "tock".

Continue this process of trial and error until the spring is correct. If the rate is only a few seconds fast in a 24 hour period, this may be corrected by the use of timing washers to add weight. (See illustration 51)

Almost all Hamilton and other high grade watches have what are known as meantime screws. These are somewhat longer than the regular time screws, and have thin short heads. (See illustrations 47 and 48) These meantime screws are usually placed near the end of the balance arm. Some watches have one pair. Some have two pairs; one set near the balance arm and the second pair placed almost midway between the balance arms.

There is a scientific reason for these screws being so placed. As a matter of fact there is a reason for everything that is done to and for the balance wheel. Our purpose here is to go into fundamentals only. After you understand the fundamentals, the finer points will be readily understood in their proper relations.

To get back to the meantime screws — you will find that they are seldom run all the way to the head. Nor should they be. To run them in changes the center of gravity and speeds up the rate. Conversely, to run them outward changes the center of gravity by increasing the circumference, and thus slows down the rate. By this you will understand that the meantime screws may be used to make small changes in the rate. It should be done only when the balance is perfectly poised. Then if a slight change is needed, move opposite meantime screws inward or outward exactly the same amount. Failure to do this, that is, to move one meantime screw more than another, will throw the balance out of poise and spoil the rate.

Rating the watch, poising the balance, and other such matters have been treated along with vibrating of the hairspring because they are so interwoven and each is so dependent on the other that they cannot be treated separately. Bear in mind that in the foregoing lesson we have tried to hit only the high spots. The essentials are given so as to give you a fair working knowledge of the spring and its functions. Only by experience can you become entirely familiar with these things. Do them over and over again until you know the reaction from every change. Learn to do every job as nearly perfect as the human equation will permit.

Strive first to do the job right. Be certain you know how to do it rather well, then strive for speed. Try doing it a little faster each time. Learn to make every move count. Never take two moves to do a job than can be done with one move. Learn to do everything from habit. Count the number of moves required to do a certain job, then try doing it in less. Look for short cuts to accomplish the same result. But NEVER SLIGHT THE WORK.

How to De-Magnetize a Watch

At one time or another, every watchmaker has had trouble with magnetism. Not much is known about where it comes from — it often occurs when no magnetic field has been contacted to the knowledge of the owner — and not much is known about getting rid of it.

In view of the present methods employed so successfully, this last statement may sound far fetched. But it is not. Every experienced workman has found, at one time or another, a watch magnetized in such a way that ordinary methods would not take it out. (See illustrations 60 to 62)

The usual method is to place a small compass over the watch suspected of magnetism. Turn the watch slowly around and watch the compass. If the balance wheel is magnetized, when the compass is directly over it the needle will rock back and forth with the swinging of the wheel. Another time it may drop directly down toward the wheel and stick in that position. On still other occasions, the compass may not be attracted to the balance but to some other part of the watch such as the stem, the crown wheel, or even the mainspring. All these things indicate magnetism. (See illustrations 63 to 65)

The simple way to remove it is with a demagnetizer which may be had from your supply house. (See illustration 66) Simply insert the watch in to the coil, press the contact button and pull the watch away at the same instant. Hold the watch on an even keel and hold the contact button until the watch is approximately three feet away from the machine. Release contact. Never at any time hold contact button more than ten seconds.

Now try the compass again. Perhaps that one effort removed it. If not, try again. Many times you must turn the watch to different positions. Perhaps the stem is magnetized. If so, it must come out through the watch. Therefore, the stem must go into the demagnetizer first, If it does not work one way, try it another. The best of demagnetizers will have to be worked with in order to remove all traces of magnetism.

Another thing to remember is this: a balance wheel that is heavily magnetized cannot be poised. Perhaps because the magnetic pole attracts the wheel such as it does a compass. So if the wheel will not poise, try the compass on it. If it is magnetized, you must remove it before continuing with the poising.

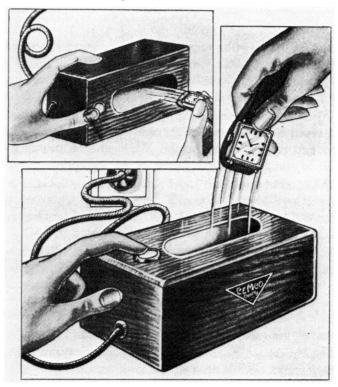

Illustration 66—Demagnetizer. Simply insert watch in coil, press contact button and pull watch away at once.

Why Many New Watches Keep Stopping

One of the most frequent causes of new watch stoppages, is oil on the hairspring. Many times newly repaired watches come back for the same reason. Usually this fault can be easily corrected. Other times it is not quite so simple.

Oil on the hairspring means just what you think it does. In some manner watch oil has run down onto the hairspring and has caused the coils to adhere to each other. This, in turn, causes the watch to stop or to run irregularly.

The condition may usually be discovered by looking at the spring with your eye loupe. If you are not certain, press one coil against another and see if it clings. Try it in three or four places around the spring, as oil might be on just a small space or two.

To remove the oil, remove the balance from the cock. Immerse the balance and spring into the cleaning solution for a few seconds. Then follow with at least two immersions in the rinsing solutions, and dry in sawdust. Remove all surplus sawdust and see if the spring will stick at any place when the coils contact each other. Magnetism may cause the spring to adhere after the oil is removed.

If the coils are clean and free, that takes care of the spring itself for the moment. But it does not remove the cause.

There are several sources from which oil may reach the spring. You must find the source in order to correct it. If the top balance jewel was not correctly oiled, oil could have run from there down the staff to the spring. To prevent this, some high grade staffs have small oil grooves cut around them just back of the pivot. This is called an oil groove.

Too much oil on the winding apparatus could have permitted a surplus to reach the center wheel which,   turn, might have carried it around to the hairspring. Proximity of the hairspring and balance to the center wheel in small watches might well bring about such contamination.

Better examine both possibilities and make the necessary corrections. Remember this, oil from the balance jewel will not — cannot — run if the cap jewel is clean and only a minute drop is placed on

Illustration 67—Clean cap jewel requires only one small drop of oil. Lack of oil causes the cap jewel to become pitted.

the cap jewel. There it should be a bubble and remain one. Only when the bubble is broken does the oil run away from the spot where it was placed. A cap jewel becomes pitted from lack of oil. (See illustration 67)

Another cause of oil running away could be a broken jewel. It might be so small that it apparently has no effect on the running of the watch. However, it will permit the oil to run away from the jewel. Even should the oil not run as far as the hairspring, the jewel being both broken and dry will score the pivot and cause almost immediate trouble. (See illustration 68)

Better replace the jewel, and staff too, if scored.

If the setting apparatus has been oiled too much and the surplus has run down and reached the spring, better remove the setting apparatus, clean it thoroughly and oil it properly and not too much.

One other word of caution. Whenever replacing balance jewels, always use the convex jewel if possible. Most good watches are fitted with convex balance jewels. But some still have the old type flat jewel, which is just what the name implies — flat. The convex jewel has a domed back. This makes it hold its oil much longer than the flat jewel. However, if the oil is always placed on the CAP jewel and is applied as instructed above, there should be little trouble in its reaching the hairspring.

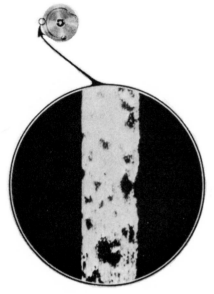

Illustration 68—Balance pivot damaged from running in dry jewel.

Illustration 69—Rust spots on hairspring cause watch to run slow. All rust must be carefully removed or a new spring used.

Common Cause of Running Slow

Frequently watches come in for repairs with the only complaint being that they run too slow. After regulating they run fine for a few weeks and repeat the same performance all over again. If you carefully check the hairspring, you will frequently find the trouble. It may have one or more spots of rust. (See illustration 69)

There are many ways of overcoming this temporarily. You may run in the meantime screws, or otherwise lighten the balance to offset the weakened spring. This is only a temporary correction. You can move the regulator. This is inadvisable, too, for the same reason. Besides, the regulator is not made to be moved. It should properly rest in the center of the index at all times in a good watch. The regulator is merely a means of holding pins on the hairspring. Perhaps you will live to see the day that better watches do not have regulators at all.

How then to correct a rusty spring?

Of course the best way is with a new spring. Occasionally for some reason that is not possible or advisable. In such cases, you must do the best you can with what you have.

If the rust spots are small and have just started, perhaps an application of oil, let them set for some time and then scrape off the rust before cleaning the spring by running briefly through your cleaning solutions.

If there are several spots but they are not yet deep enough to greatly effect the running of the watch, the spring may be boiled for a few minutes in penetrating oil or a good grade fish oil. Then let cool and clean in the usual manner. This should stop the erosion of the rust, then you have only to compensate for the weakened spring by adjusting the weight of the balance. If the spring is very rusty and the erosion has eaten in, a new spring is the only practical solution.

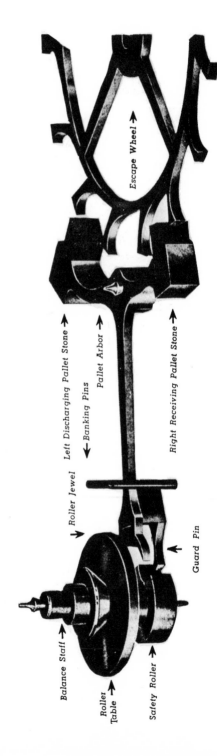

Escape Wheel →

Left Discharging Pallet Stone →

← Banking Pins

Pallet Arbor →

Right Receiving Pallet Stone →

→ Roller Jewel

Guard Pin ←

Balance Staff →

Roller Table →

Safety Roller →

Illustration 70—Watch escapement, showing relative position of parts and their correct Names.

While on the subject of rust, keep in mind that it is the enemy of all fine parts and should be removed whenever encountered. During the summer months, stems and setting parts are particularly subject to rust. When this condition is encountered, all rust should be removed promptly, and then the watch cleaned.

Setting parts may be quickly cleaned of rust — provided it has just begun rusting — by holding them against a brass scratch brush turning at a moderate rate of speed. The brush will not damage the steel. However, if the rust was caused by salt water or has already made considerable headway, better remove each part and replace it with a new one if possible. If that is not possible, then use an emery buff to remove all rust down to the polished steel.

After all rust has been removed, use the brass brush on the watch plates. All parts should now be thoroughly oiled, but not too much oil used. This should keep the rust down.

As a safety measure for wrist watches that are inclined to rust easily, perhaps a small amount of good clean cup grease should be used around the stem where it goes into the movement. This does not look so good, but if it keeps out water and prevents rust trouble, it is worthwhile.

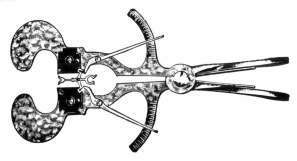

Illustration 71—Pallet stone setter and adjusting tool. Work can be executed without guesswork and without danger of injury to jewels or lever. Holds them rigid and level.

Locating Watch Troubles

In preceding lessons we have been dealing with the hairspring as a separate unit. Since it is so closely related to the escapement, and since many actions on one will have reactions on the other, we shall now take up the study of the escapement itself. (See illustration 70)

Before starting this lesson study illustration 70 carefully. Note the names and positions of each part. At first the drawing may be so much Greek. But as you study it, locate each item in the watch on which you are now working. This will help you visualize the escapement as a whole and its relation to the watch as a whole. Remember that each part has a certain function to perform. In order to properly perform that function, each part must work in unison with every other part.

As we go along with this lesson we shall go back to this drawing from time to time. Each time you will observe something new; something you could have seen before had you known where to look and what you were looking for. When you can look at this drawing and learn something from it each time, you will know that you are making progress.

As you become more skilled, more proficient in your work, you will find that many times the biggest job of all is in "locating the trouble". That is particularly true of the escapement. That, too, is the reason for paying particular attention to this drawing and to the lessons that follow. You must know how a thing should be, otherwise how will you know when it is correct?

By this time you should have learned to have great pride in your work. It is not only a needed work, but it is one requiring the highest skill. Like a physician, you spend an indefinite time, wear out several sets of nerves, spend a lot of money, learning your profession. See that you do nothing that will discredit that profession. You are now well on your way.

Just as the most difficult job of a physician is the diagnosis, so it is with the watchmaker. The doctor must first find why a patient is ill. He has many ways of doing this. The X-ray. The fluoroscope. Blood tests. And dozens of other methods he uses to locate and segregate the trouble spot. The better physician uses the most up-to-the-minute methods he can get. So it must be with you.

After the physician has correctly diagnosed the disease, the correction is often very simple. So it is with the watchmaker. He, too,

Illustration 72—Metric roller jewel system. Contains 210 Garnet roller jewels (6 each of 35 separate metric sizes) that fit all sizes of watches; Baguette, Wrist and Pocket. A chart with a complete listing of all makes and sizes by metric system is included, making the selection of a proper size roller jewel a simple, easy matter. Correct size of roller jewel needed is quickly determined by inserting arm of gauge in slot of fork, without removing fork from movement. The number on arm of gauge indicates the correct metric size of roller jewel needed.

must know intimately every part of the watch's anatomy. Know what its particular function is. He must know when it is in the correct relation to every other part. Then when he begins looking for the trouble, his trained eye will tell him when he has found it. Often the eye alone will not tell. He must use his ears. And if any modern machines are available to assist him, he must learn to use them to his advantage.

All this is a prelude to the first lesson on the escapement. You cannot be overly impressed with the importance of the escapement of a watch. Once again it may truthfully be said, if the escapement is wrong, everything is wrong. It is the one part that must be right at all times. Otherwise you are certain to have trouble.

The escapement consists of the following parts: escape wheel, pallet fork and arbor, pallet stones, pallet bridge, balance assembly including roller jewel, guard pin, banking pins. The drawing presented here shows the parts enlarged many times. Each one is named. Study these names carefully and memorize each one. Notice where and how it is located and pay particular attention to the particular part it plays. (See illustrations 4 and 5)

Now, take your 16 size Hamilton movement again and let us adjust the escapement.

First, notice the peculiar shape of the teeth of the escape wheel. Observe that as the watch runs, the escape wheel acts as a conveyor

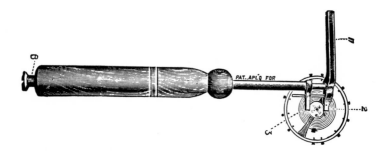

Illustration 73—Combination tool. It is shown here as a roller jewel setter. Can be adapted equally well to holding hands, jewels in settings; also can be used for setting pallet jewels.

of the power of the train to the balance wheel by way of the pallet fork. As the escape wheel teeth strike the impulse face of the pallet stones, the train power kicks the fork over until it rests against the other banking pin. This fork, in turn, through its action with the roller jewel, swings the balance around in an arc. The reaction of the hairspring brings it back.

To express it another way, and to try to make it entirely clear to you, the hairspring is striving constantly to bring the roller jewel to rest along the line of centers. The fork and escapement are determined it shall not come to rest there. This action and reaction makes the watch run.

Closely observe the construction of the two pallet stones. The first stone to contact a given tooth is known as the receiving stone.

This is usually on the right side of the fork as you look at it in the watch; hence it is often called the right pallet stone. Observe that the end of the stone which contacts the escape tooth is polished and the end is cut at an angle. This is known as the impulse face. Notice the degree of angle of this impulse face.

The stone on the left side of the fork is known as the "left" or discharging stone. Notice that the degree of angle of its impulse face is somewhat sharper than that of the receiving stone. This is important. It must always be thus.

For reasons of brevity, we shall hereafter refer to the pallet stones simply as right or left. Remember, however, that the receiving stone is always right, and the discharging stone is always left, even should the escape wheel turn counter clockwise and the stones be reversed in the pallet.

The 16 size Hamilton with which we are working is a standard watch. That is to say the receiving stone is on the right; the discharging stone is on the left. Now remove the balance assembly and have a little power on the train. Catch the fork gently in the tweezer points and observe the action of the fork and the stones on the escape wheel. Gently move the fork away from the banking pin toward the line of centers. As you do so observe that the escape tooth moves down the pallet stone until it reaches the impulse face of the stone. At that exact point the entire power of the train rests against the face of the stone; this impulse causes the fork to jump quickly to the opposite banking pin. Move it away from that pin, and the action is repeated in the other direction.

Now to proceed, remove the hands and dial. Through the bottom plate just back of each pallet stone is a hole large enough to see the entire stone action through. By looking through these openings you can often observe actions that are obscured by the balance when observed from the other side.

Next remove only the hairspring from the balance wheel, and place the wheel with roller table back into position in the watch. Tighten the balance cock. Now watch carefully the pallet fork and roller jewel action as you slowly turn the balance wheel with one finger. Notice, too, the slot in the safety roller. The guard pin or plunger in the fork must point directly into this slot when the roller jewel is facing squarely into the fork and the fork is resting along the line of centers.

Use a good eye loupe to observe the action as you follow these instructions. They are to familiarize you with the correct action of the entire escapement. With one finger on the balance wheel bring it slowly toward the slot of the fork. Notice how the roller jewel passes the horn of the fork and crosses the slot and contacts the other side. Stop. Notice it strikes the slot well below the cover of the fork horn. Now move it back slowly until the roller jewel is at its nearest point to the prong of the fork. Make a mental note of the amount of tolerance there. The roller jewel should just NOT touch the horn of the fork as it comes into the slot.

The tolerances allowed here vary with the individual watch. But it is safe to say that the roller jewel must just clear. To test this clearance, stop the balance as the roller jewel faces the receiving fork. Hold the balance firmly with one hand and with a tweezer move the fork back and forth at this point. You can see how much clearance it has by the amount of play in the fork as it moves between the roller jewel on one side and the banking pin on the other. This tolerance must be the same on either side.

The Escapement --- How to Understand it

Thus far we have simply been studying the escapment and its actions. Assuming that the watch we have as an experiment is correct, we should have learned many things that heretofore have been obscure to us. If the watch movement you have is not correct in the escapement action, perhaps you have found where it is out. Good. You are making progress. Remember, you must first learn to know when it is wrong, and where. Only then can you begin making the necessary corrections. Never attempt to make a correction until you are certain one is needed there. To do so only brings on more trouble that will eventually have to be corrected.

In the previous lesson when we were watching the fork escape, we paid no particular attention to the position of the stones. We will do so now. Observe that the stones are set in a small slot in the pallet. On the bottom of each is a very small spot of shellac. This holds the stone firmly in place. The rear ends of the pallet stones may or may not rest in the bottom or back of the slots. That in itself does not matter.

To know when a thing is correct is one thing. To know when it is incorrect is another thing; to know how to make it correct when it is incorrect is the important thing. We are coming to that now.

In the previous lesson we examined the tolerance of the pallet fork. Now observe the banking pins. These are the two pins, one of which the fork rests against at all times when it is inert. Turn the watch over and observe that each banking pin is cut eccentrically on a screw that is set in the plate. Now place a small screwdriver in the screw slot and turn the screw just one fourth turn while observing the pin on the other side of the plate. Being eccentric on the screw, the pin swings toward the fork when turned one way. It swings away from the fork when turned the other way.

In adjusting the escapement we are going to work from the balance outward. Turn the banking pins inward on either side of the fork. Turn them in first until the balance will not turn. That is, the roller jewel will strike the prong as it comes into the fork. Now turn the banking pins back outward until the roller jewel will just clear the prong. Test it as described in the previous lesson and reduce the tolerance almost to that irreducible minimum. When the tolerance, at the very instant the stone faces the prong, is just enough to permit freedom and no more on either side, observe the action of the guard pin. Does it touch the safety roller when the jewel is not facing the fork? Is it free at all positions of the balance? If not, better give the roller jewel a little more tolerance by opening the banking pins just as much as necessary, and no more. Of course, the guard pin must be perfectly straight and even between the prongs, and free of burrs. It should just clear the safety roller with an absolute minimum of side shake. Set the banking pins at this point and leave them there.

Now turn the watch over, observing the action of the escape teeth on the stones through the bottom plate while slowly turning the balance wheel back and forth with the finger.

While doing this, the escape teeth should strike the pallet stone just back of the impulse face a distance equal to approximately one-fourth the width of the impulse face of the stone. It should also strike the stone at the exact instant the fork strikes the banking pin. This is called "banked to drop".

Banked to drop literally means that the escape tooth drops against the stone, and the fork drops against the banking pin at the same instant.

By the fork striking the pin at the instant the escape tooth strikes the pallet stone, the tooth does not slide on the stone. Striking back of the impulse face it immediately locks the escapement. Hence this is called the lock. The distance which it strikes back of the face is called the depth of lock.

If, in escaping, the tooth strikes the impulse face of the stone, it does not lock; cannot lock. Therefore, the fork attempts to swing back to the other stone. If the same action takes place on the other stone, the fork swings back and forth of its own accord. That is, the escapement is not locking. When the balance is in the watch, the fork cannot swing all the way back, because on its reverse it strikes the roller jewel. Therefore, the watch cannot run as it should. To correct it, you simply make each stone lock the escapement.

Now to go back to the spot where we had the watch banked to drop. Try opening the banking pins just a small fraction of a turn. When you have opened both an equal amount, turn the wheel slowly again and observe that when the stone strikes the escape tooth, the fork has not yet reached the banking pin.

Now let the balance continue its arc and note that the escape tooth slides up on the stone just a hair's breadth. This is called the slide. The distance of the slide is called the depth of slide.

It is well that the amount of slide should not exceed a distance equal to the lock. That is, after the lock and slide, the tooth rests back of the impulse face not more than a distance equal to one-half the impulse face.

To put it another way, when the slide is complete and the fork rests against the banking pin, the escape tooth is back of the impulse face of the stone a distance not more than twice what it was the instant it first locked, or the instant the tooth first struck the stone.

To prove the point, open only one banking pin. Increase the depth of slide distance equal to the length of the impulse face. Now bring the balance around from that side until the roller jewel contacts the slot of the fork, and observe the effort to make the watch escape. Additional power must be brought on it to make the escapement unlock.

The reason is twofold. First, the stone is so slanted that to reach the impulse face where it can escape, the power of the hairspring must force the entire train backward against the power of the train. Notice the backward motion of the escape wheel before it begins to unlock the escapement.

Secondly, there is the roller jewel action to consider. When it comes into the slot properly, it strikes the inside of the slot, not just the horn. With the banking pins so wide open, the fork is so far away from the line of centers that the roller jewel comes not into the slot, but strikes the horn. Then it cannot unlock the escapement.

Observe this closely and see just what action is taking place here. Then close the banking pin to the proper position and note the difference in the fork action.

Adjusting the Escapement

Thus far in the series of lessons on the escapement, we have dealt largely with general conditions. By this time you should have a very good perspective of the escapement and the part it plays in the watch. But you are just beginning to learn. No doubt you now feel that you really know the escapement. That is fine. It builds confidence. But no matter how much confidence you have, never make up your mind you know it all. When you do that, you stop learning. To be a good watchmaker — or a success at anything else, for that matter — you must never stop learning. You never learn it all. That is merely the goal you strive to attain.

In dealing with the escapement, we must of necessity deal in generalities. We cannot hope to take every possible escapement trouble and show you how to correct it. That would require a large book in itself. Nor do I think it desirable to do that. What you want to do is learn the escapement so well that you can make whatever correction you may encounter.

To help you reach that state of perfection, let's produce a given situation — one encountered more or less frequently in bench work — and proceed to find the trouble and correct it.

Take again the 16 size Hamilton watch. See that it is running properly. First we must create the situation by making some changes in the escapement, much as another workman might do. To do this and to correct the trouble after you have made it, you must learn to use another tool. This is the pallet stone setter. (See illustration 71)

The pallet stone setter opens much like a pair of scissors. It has adjustable jaws for holding any size pallet fork while the work is being done. Before trying to use it, remove the two adjusting levers shown on top. This may be a good idea, but it is just in your way. Take them off. The one other thing you will need is a small alcohol lamp.

Remove the pallet fork from the watch. Turn it bottom side up on the bench. As you look at it now, bottom side up, remember the left stone is on the right side. The right stone is on the left side. Open the jaws of the stone setting tool, and place the fork bottom side up in the jaws. Let the spring close the jaws gently, seeing that the pallet stones come to rest flatly on the base of the tool.

Being held thus, the fork should point toward the handles of the tool; the stones point away from the handles. When the pallet is secure and the tension of the tool will hold it in place, observe carefully the appearance of the fork from the bottom. Note carefully the depth of each stone in its slot. Do they go all the way back? Are they out an equal distance?

Knowing that the watch was running correctly before moving the pallet fork, we shall assume that the stones are not quite to the back of the slots, but are each set out an equal distance. Now, to create a situation, let's push one of the stones away from the back of the slot a distance approximately twice that of the other one.

Do this by catching the tool by the handles — not tight enough to release the fork — and holding the other end over a small alcohol flame. Hold it just long enough to warm the shellac holding the stone in place. (Hold only one side over the flame and only one stone will become warm.) When the shellac is warm enough to become somewhat soft, use the point of a needle or a small screwdriver to slip behind the stone and gently push the stone outward. Do this carefully so the stone does not come all the way out of the pallet. Be certain that the stone is still flat and in line with the other.

When the shellac is cool, replace the fork in the watch and observe that it does not escape. Perhaps you moved the right stone. (It was on the left when the fork was bottom side up.) If so, you will observe that the left stone still strikes the tooth in the usual manner. It locks just as it should. It unlocks as it should, but yet the escape wheel does not escape.

To carry the experiment still further, open the banking pin on the right side and permit the stone to escape. Then you will notice that what has happened is the escape tooth cannot reach the impulse face of the stone. By opening the banking pin on that side, you have made it possible for the impulse face to reach the face of the tooth, so it escapes.

Now put the balance in the watch and see if it will run. Chances are it will not run at all. If it does manage to run, note its very poor motion. Change it into positions and see if it does not stop entirely. Should it by some chance continue to run, set it and note the variation in time. In short, it will not — cannot — keep time in this condition.

Correction of Escapement Faults

In the foregoing lesson we created a condition which is often found in watches in the regular run of repairs. You created this condition for a purpose. Remember, many workmen do this and worse, not knowing that they are creating an impossible condition — and what is more, not knowing how to correct it.

Very well, we know the condition of the escapement now. We know it because we created it. Forget for a moment that you have ever seen this watch before. Assume that it was brought to you for repairs and you found it in this condition. How would you go about locating the trouble and correcting it?

Let's remove the hairspring again and replace the balance in the watch. By placing the finger against the balance wheel and turning slowly around again, we find these faults.

Roller jewel does not come into fork properly.

Escape teeth do not strike pallet stones properly.

Both stones have too much slide. One stone has more slide than the other.

Watch has very poor motion or will not run at all.

Roller jewel and fork tolerances are not equal.

These are the faults. How do you go about correcting them? Put yourself in the position of a watchmaker in a fine jewelry store or shop. This watch has just been brought in for repairs. Perhaps it belongs to a very good customer. He has had it repaired all over town, and yet it does not run as it should.

Under such circumstances you would be very anxious to do your very best work. Very well, now do your very best work. See if you remember how to locate the trouble.

I hope that you remember your previous lessons well enough

that you have already located and corrected the trouble. If you have forgotten, proceed as follows.

First, bring the banking pins in until the roller jewel just clears the fork on either side, leaving only enough tolerance to be free as it enters and leaves the fork. Check the guard pin too. It must be free of the safety roller in order to test the tolerance of the roller jewel.

When the watch is banked to drop, the escapement will not unlock. See how easy it is to locate the trouble? Before closing the banking pins the eye had fooled you. It looked then as if the left stone was the one to be moved inward. But now with the banking pins closed to the allowed tolerances, you can see that the right stone has locked the escapement completely and will not unlock it That, then, is where the trouble is bound to be.

Knowing where the trouble is, it is a simple matter to move the pallet fork, place it once again in the stone setter and adjust it to its proper position. Two or three efforts may be necessary to get it just right, remembering that to be just right now it must escape though banked to drop.

When it is moved back to the proper depth, the shellac is set and the two pallet stones are flat and perfectly in line, open the banking pins just enough to permit a little slide. Now place the balance wheel in the watch and notice how freely it runs and the quick, snappy motion it has.

What to Do With the Banking Pins

Before leaving the pallet stones, you should create and note the reaction of at least one other fault. You could go on creating faults one after another, and correcting them. In fact, that is a good suggestion. Create a few of your own. See how many different things you can do to a pallet fork, and then correct it.

Next move the fork from the watch. We are assuming again that you have it correct. Very well. When we left the fork each pallet stone was not quite back to the bottom of its slot. Heat the fork once again in the usual manner and push each stone as far back as it will go.

Now place the fork in the watch and put a little power on the train. Notice what a poor motion the balance takes. No matter how you try, the motion remains poor and the watch stops in positions. This means it cannot keep accurate time.

All we did was move the stones back in their slots.

This, in turn, set them away from the escape wheel so they could not lock. To test this, remove the balance and test the fork by moving it back and forth a few times. Notice that the escape teeth are striking the impulse face. It cannot lock, no matter if the banking pins are opened. Unless the escapement locks, the watch cannot run properly. The reason is obvious.

This is a small thing, to be sure. But it can cause a lot of trouble. In this case, fortunately, you know what to do to correct it. But what if you found this condition in a watch which you had not seen before? What then?

Go back to fundamentals. Place the balance wheel minus the hairspring back into the watch. (By using the balance without the hairspring you are able to see the roller and pallet action. Later, you can do much of this with the spring in place) Move the balance back and forth slowly, just far enough to make the escapement unlock. Observe the pallet action through the peep holes in the plate. Notice that when the tooth strikes the impulse face, the fork immediately starts its backward swing toward the other banking pin. When it does this, notice the action of the roller jewel.

Instead of the balance continuing on with its regular arc, the fork kicks back, striking the roller jewel and causing the balance to stop or lose momentum.

Of course it is corrected in the usual manner. When the banking pins are set up until it is "banked to drop", you will observe that each stone is so set that the escape tooth strikes the impulse face. It does not lock. Obviously, then, the stone should be moved outward just enough to make it lock properly. That is, lock at the instant the fork strikes the banking pin. Then when the necessary slide is given, the escapement locks and unlocks as it should. Now notice the difference in the motion of the watch.

In this lesson and the one preceding it we have done a lot of moving of the banking pins. It was done for a purpose. You must be familiar with every part of the escapement. The position of the pallet stones are very important, so are the banking pins which help to govern them. But remember this, banking pins must be moved only for a purpose.

The pins should be turned so that they are toward the slot of the fork. This rule does not always hold true, but most always it does. That is to say, when the pins are correctly set, they are toward the slot end of the fork rather than toward the arm of the fork.

Remember, too, that it is seldom necessary to turn a banking pin more than one-fourth turn of the head. Use the proper size screwdriver blade and do not mar the screw head. Above all, do not begin turning the banking screws hoping that will make the necessary correction. It will not.

If a watch has been properly handled, regardless of its age, it is seldom necessary to touch the banking screws. If every watchmaker would remember that and observe it, a lot of time and trouble could be avoided for all of us. Be certain that you keep it in mind. Move the banking pins only when absolutely necessary, and then only for one purpose.

Setting and Adjusting the Roller Jewel

The roller jewel plays a very important part in the time keeping performance of a watch. In any study of the escapement, the importance of the roller jewel cannot be overlooked. However, taken by and large, it gives comparatively little trouble.

In our previous studies we have worked with the escapement largely from the other end. And all conditions set forth in previous lessons were predicated on the assumption that the roller jewel was correct at the time. That is why this lesson is an important part of the study of the escapement.

If the roller jewel is properly set and securely shellacked, it will not give trouble. However, in any escapement trouble it is well to examine the roller jewel first. Examine it for the following points:

Securely set. That is, not loose in the setting.

Setting perpendicular when viewed from every angle.

That it does not reach down to the safety roller on the double roller models.

That all surplus shellac has been removed from the roller and the jewel itself.

That the jewel is not broken and its edges are smooth.

The flat side of the jewel must face squarely into the fork.

Just for the experience and training, as well as for the actual "know how" obtained, let's go ahead and set a roller jewel.

The first tool used here is a roller jewel gauge. (See illustration 72) This is really a series of gauges in one. Each blade is numbered. Open these blades out until you have access to several. Choose the one that seems nearest the size needed to fit snugly into the jewel slot or fork. It should fit not tight, but with very close tolerance. Then notice the number stamped on this blade. Perhaps it is number 40. In any event, select a jewel from the system that is two numbers smaller. If the number on the gauge is 40, select a jewel from bottle number 38. This difference in numbers allows for the tolerances that the roller jewel must have.

Now that you have the jewel selected, there are many approved ways of getting it into the roller. The one outlined here probably calls for the greatest amount of skill, which is what you want.

First clean all shellac from the hole in the roller. Then take the balance wheel in the fingers of the left hand. Use the fine point of your hairspring tweezers to handle the jewel. Here extreme care must be used. Jewels often flip out of the tweezer points of experienced workmen. So do not be discouraged if you lose a few jewels at first.

The object is to catch the jewel in the tweezers with the flat side of the jewel facing you. Then slip the end of the jewel into the hole in the roller. When the end is started and the jewel will set upright, gently ease your grip on the jewel and take the tweezers away. If it fits snugly — and it should — push it down until what is now the lower end is flush with the back side of the roller table. Be sure to push it down enough so that what is now in the inverted position, is the upper end, clears the safety roller. This is necessary in order that the jewel will clear the safety or guard pin on the fork. When these tolerances are set, you are ready to take up the use of still another tool — the roller jewel setter. (See illustration 73)

The use of this tool will be explained in just a moment. But before we come to that, bear in mind that some rollers may have been tampered with and the jewel hold may have been enlarged. In that case, the jewel which is correct for the fork may be too small to properly fit the roller table. In a case of this kind it is better to follow shop practice.

Many good shops will automatically replace this bad roller with a new one. However, when material is difficult to obtain, this may not always be practical.

This condition will occasionally be found in obsolete watches and the rollers cannot be replaced readily, or else the price for doing the job will not justify the added expense such a move would entail. In either case, we must make the best use we can of what we have. This means setting a roller jewel in a roller with a large jewel hole.

Before proceeding, make certain the jewel is as large as the fork will accommodate. Place it in the roller even though it is loose and let it set as it will until the shellac has flowed around it. Then with the shellac slightly warm, adjust the jewel to its proper position.

The roller jewel setter is a simple tool, designed to be worked with one hand — the left. By pushing the button on the very end of the handle, you opened the jaws. Close the jaws gently on either side of the roller table. The spring tension will now hold the balance while the work is being done.

Have a piece of shredded jewel shellac handy while the table is being heated. When that part of the flame above the heating unit changes color, the table should be hot enough to apply the shellac.

Here, too, several methods are used. The cleanest job is obtained by touching the very end of the shred of shellac to the jewel hole on the back of the roller. That is to say, the side of the roller away from the jewel. If the roller is clean and free of grease and oil, a touch of shellac should do a neat, secure job provided the roller was hot enough. Caution: do not overheat it.

If the jewel is not tight in the roller, see that the hole is well filled with shellac and adjust the jewel to its proper position while the shellac is yet warm. Once it is set, it must be warmed again in order to move the jewel. When the jewel is setting upright, steady, and in perfect order, release the balance and permit it to cool before placing in the watch.

Frequent Cause of Poor, Sluggish Motion

You have learned to select and set a roller jewel. As you do this job over and over your eyes and hands become more coordinated and it becomes just another routine job. However, after each roller jewel setting, the escapement must be checked again. The roller jewel plays an important part there.

Here is a condition to look for: the watch is banked to drop, and there is too much tolerance as the jewel comes into the fork.

Perhaps you have set the jewel, but on examining the escapement you find this condition. It may be — and often is indicated by a watch that has a poor, sluggish motion. Examine all parts of the escapement, and when you have traced the trouble to this condition, here is how to correct it.

We know that the watch is banked to drop. Therefore, the tolerance as the roller jewel comes into the fork should be very close. So as it leaves the fork. Yet the tolerance is too much. The watch has a very poor motion and stops occasionally. There can be just one trouble. The roller jewel should lean more toward the fork.

Place the balance in the roller jewel tool and warm it just enough to make the shellac soft. Insert a fine needle point back of the roller jewel and give it a gentle outward pressure. The object is to slant the jewel forward, thus reducing the tolerance in the fork as the jewel enters it.

A little change here will make a big difference.

Occasionally, too, you will find an opposite condition. The jewel will be leaning outwardly too much. If the watch is banked to drop and still the roller jewel binds going into and leaving the fork, the jewel may need adjusting. First try giving the stones just a little slide. If the roller jewel still binds on the horns of the fork, by all means slant it back just enough to permit it to clear at the binding points.

You may have to move it several times before you find the correct place.

Another good thing to remember is that if the watch runs accurately, apparently the escapement is correct as it is. But it is well to check it to be sure. But make no changes unless they are indicated. In a factory escapement that is correct throughout, the roller jewel is set perpendicular. That is, leans neither forward nor backward, nor right nor left.

If you have cleaned or otherwise repaired a watch and it does not take a good motion, you know it cannot keep time. But do not "assume" that this or that is wrong, and start opening or closing banking pins or making other adjustments. You will most likely be doing the wrong thing and will only have to undo it later anyway.

If you are convinced that everything else is correct, and have traced the sluggishness or stoppage to the escapement, then start at the beginning and check everything.

Sometimes a loose roller jewel will cause the watch to stop, or vary, or have a sluggish motion. To the eye it looks to be okeh, but better test it with your tweezer. It may play back and forth, yet not come out.

If the shellac has just worked loose, a simple heating will often suffice. Add a little more shellac if necessary.

If a jewel has to be slanted forward or backward so it will enter the fork properly, as described a few paragraphs above, it is due to a change having been made previously. Perhaps the fork has been replaced by one just a little short. Or maybe the roller table has been replaced with one a fraction smaller. Any such changes made by you or anyone else, require subsequent changes to offset the error.

Understanding the Two Kinds of Rollers

No doubt you have observed that there are two kinds of rollers: double roller and single roller. The 16s watch on which we have been working is a double roller. However, there are still quite a few single rollers in service and you will often be called on to repair one of this type. Therefore, it is well to know just how to handle it when you find one.

First, if the watch you happen to be working on at any given time is a single roller model, escapement adjusting is somewhat different than it is in the conventional double roller model.

I believe the terms, Single Roller and Double Roller, are self-explanatory. If they are not, remember that the single roller has only one roller. The double roller is just what the name implies — double roller.

On the single roller pallet fork the safety pin stands upright at the seat of the fork. This pin is just long enough that it comes directly into the safety SLOT at the exact instant of escaping. And on this type watch, remember always in adjusting the escapement and testing the tolerance of the roller jewel as it comes into the fork, this safety pin should be straightened up until there is no possibility of its catching the edge of the slot and thus making the tolerance appear less than it actually is.

After the banking pins are properly set and the roller jewel tolerance is correct, then the safety pin should be bent toward the roller until it comes well within the slot when the jewel is square within the fork. Yet it must clear the roller as it goes into and comes out of the fork.

There is a definite reason for this. It could be explained, but a better way to remember its dangers is to actually demonstrate the fault. Do this by straightening the safety pin until it stands exactly upright. Now let the watch run in a normal manner for a few seconds. Then take a pair of good tweezers and grasp the center wheel by one spoke and push it sharply backward hard enough to reverse the entire train of the watch. Do this two or three times, if necessary.

No doubt the very first time you tried it the watch stopped and refused to run when you tried to start it up. If so, you will observe that the roller jewel has jumped out of the pallet fork, and before starting the watch again you must take the entire balance out of the watch and replace it correctly. Now try this same action and observe closely the action of the pallet fork and roller jewel. When the pressure is applied, the train wheels in reverse force the pallet fork to reverse its course abruptly, thus causing it to swing away from the roller jewel. This stops the watch. And this is what will happen when the watch is set or if it gets a slight jar while in the wearer's pocket or on his arm. The condition is called over-banking.

To correct this, push the safety pin back just far enough that when pressure is placed against the train, the safety pin comes into the safety slot and catches on the roller, thus preventing the fault described above.

With the double roller such as the 16s watch we have at hand, the action is slightly different in application, but exactly the same in principle. It differs in that the safety pin is underneath the fork and comes out under the roller jewel slot; in short, making a three pronged fork. The small safety roller is so arranged that it does the same duty as the single roller described above.

The difference in adjusting the double roller is that it causes less trouble in the first place, and the safety pin cannot so easily be adjusted in the second place.

It should be stated here that unless a pallet fork or a roller table has to be replaced in a watch, there is seldom any reason for changing the safety pin of the double roller watch; the exception being when adjusting the escapement. Should such a change be necessary — and it may be ascertained just as with the single roller — the correction is made by pushing the safety pin back toward the roller. Bear in mind, when this action is necessary, that by moving the pin an amount so small the eye cannot detect it, will many times be all that is necessary. Should the safety pin be so tightly fitted in the fork that it cannot be moved, there is another method sometimes used.

That is a lengthening of the pin itself. This is to be used as a last resort, and is not to be considered the proper method of making this correction. Observe that the safety pin is pointed somewhat like a carpenter's nail. If it is necessary to make a small adjustment in the length of the pin, perhaps just a slight squeezing of the point with a pair of flat nosed, smooth jawed, pliers will stretch the pin sufficiently.

If such a process is tried, be sure to reshape the end of the pin when you are through, to approximately its exact shape and position before the stretching was done. A very slight burr on the safety pin may cause trouble in the escapement. It will cause the watch to stop, vary in time, and perhaps do many other things that you will find hard to explain.

In the previous lesson on setting the roller jewel, I stressed the importance of seeing that the jewel was so set that it cleared the safety pin. This particular feature is just as important regardless of whether you set the roller jewel. Therefore, it should be checked. If the staff has very much end shake — that is, if the staff plays up and down in its jewels — it may drop down until the end of the roller jewel strikes the safety pin. Some watches will do this occasionally, but when tried they seem to clear properly. Therefore, we find it essential that everything be right. The end shake must be correct — just enough to make the balance absolutely free in the jewels and no more. Then the safety pin must be just low enough to free the roller jewel in all positions. But it must not be so low that is misses the safety roller.

Another point not to be overlooked is the amount of end shake in the pallet arbor. Too much end shake here will permit the fork to drop toward the balance when the watch is face down. If it drops enough, the pallet fork may touch the roller. Or the safety pin may touch the roller jewel. Either of these faults will cause the watch to stop.

How to Put the Watch in Beat

No study of the escapement is quite complete without a few words on getting the watch in beat. In a previous lesson we covered this subject very briefly by instructing you to see that the roller jewel is on a direct line of centers with the balance jewel, pallet jewel, and escape wheel jewel. In other words, see that it squarely faces the pallet fork and comes to rest directly between the two banking pins. This is good advice. But it is not always enough.

If you have adjusted the escapement from start to finish, then the above instructions will be sufficient. Many times, however, you will find a watch whose escapement is not out enough to affect its running or time keeping, yet with roller jewel placed as instructed it will still be out of beat.

Remember that being out of beat means just this: The "tick" and the "tock" should be of the exact duration. If they are not; that is, the "tick" is longer than the "tock" or vice versa, that is called being out of beat. The best way to detect this error is by listening closely to the watch while it is running, changing positions occasionally as you do so.

When this condition exists, we must determine which way it is out. One method is to try stopping the balance wheel by holding the finger against it gently. If it will stop and remain stopped in any position, note which side of center the pallet fork rests. Change position of roller jewel until the fork comes to rest directly between the pins and then the watch will not stop. A watch that is in perfect condition, escapement correct, and in perfect beat, will not stop. No matter where you may stop the balance, when it is released it will immediately kick off and pick up motion very quickly. This is due to the fact that a watch in perfect beat always has one tooth of the escape wheel resting against the impulse face of a pallet stone when the balance is inert, or when roller jewel comes to rest between the banking pins.

This fact alone shows us that we must use the position of the pallet stones to determine the correct "beat". To do this we first release the mainspring, thus removing the power from the train. We leave the balance in position and let it come to rest where it will. It is best, also, to remove the dial so we can use the openings behind the pallet stones to look at the stones.

Now lay the watch in a flat position so we can watch the stones as we use a tweezer to bring just a little pressure on the train. Do this by pressing the center wheel very lightly. When this is done, the escape tooth should strike the impulse face of the right stone approximately in the center of the face. The escape tooth should strike the left stone just PAST the center of the impulse face. If it does not do this, simply change the position of the roller jewel until it does do it.

As explained in a previous lesson, you change the position of the roller jewel by changing not the jewel — but the position of the hairspring collet. Since the hairspring always fits on the cock in the exact same position, any change in the position of its collet makes a corresponding change in the relative position of the roller jewel. The collet position is changed by inserting a sharp instrument in the opening of the hairspring collet, and turning it to the right or left as desired, until the roller jewel comes to rest in the correct position.

The Mainspring---"Motor" of the Watch

You are now familiar enough with the watch and its working parts to realize the importance of the mainspring. It is to the watch as a motor is to an automobile. In fact, it is the motive power of the watch.

No doubt you have often heard it referred to as the main string, or the winding string, or perhaps winding chain. Perhaps these terms have some justification, in fact. For the English some years back built a watch with a winding chain. Some of them are still in use today. However, most of the terms in use today are corruptions of the simple word, Mainspring. It, be it noted, is actually two words. But in general usage when the main spring of a watch is meant, it is written as one word.

The mainspring, you have noticed, is enclosed in a barrel. This is the mainspring barrel. Inside this barrel is an arbor which works in the inside coil of the spring. This is a barrel arbor. On this barrel goes a barrel head.

When the spring is fully wound, the spring is in the center of the barrel tightly wound around the barrel arbor. When it is in run-down condition, it is resting against the outside of the barrel. Thus we will see that the spring must be the proper length. If it is too long, thus filling the barrel too full, the watch will not run 24 hours. If it is too short, it will give the same result.

At first thought, that will sound like an impossibility. If the spring were not in a barrel, the longer the spring the longer the watch would run with one winding. The barrel, however, makes the difference. When the spring is down, it is still all confined within the space of the barrel. Therefore, a spring an inch or two too long may mean two or three times around the barrel, thus filling it up too quickly, causing a run down condition. The spring is run down when it will no longer exert pressure on the train.

Next let us observe that the mainspring barrel is the first wheel, the center wheel is the second wheel, and so on to the escape wheel. The escape wheel is actually the 5th wheel of the train, but is usually referred to simply as the escape wheel. Likewise the center wheel is the second wheel, but is known simply as the center wheel. The barrel is the first wheel, but is always known as the mainspring barrel.

The mainspring barrel is so simple in construction that it may be likened to a checker board in that it is so simple it is complicated. Checkers look like the most simple of all games of skill. Yet their very simplicity make them difficult to play with skill. I am told that a good checker player must be able to see sixteen plays ahead at all times. And this when every play looks exactly like the other.

This condition also exists to a certain degree with the mainspring and barrel. It looks to be the most simple part of the watch. But let me warn you to follow this lesson closely and see that you fully understand everything about it before passing on to the next. Do not forget that you also have to deal with the idiosyncrasies of a tempered piece of steel operating under all conditions and temperatures. (See illustrations 74 to 76)

Merely replacing a spring would be a small job if everyone replaced the broken spring each time with the correct spring. Since that is not the case, however, we must many times know what should be the correct spring or we are lost. We must know how to find the correct spring, how to fit it.

Since many watchmakers change springs often when it is not necessary and then fit the wrong spring, too, it is good practice to have a complete mainspring chart for all watches and go strictly by this chart when fitting or changing a spring. Such a chart is available on all well known makes of watches. In general repairs you will find that there is no chart available for many watches, and perhaps the spring in the watch is not the correct one.

Well, you may ask, how do we know when a spring is not the correct one? This is sometimes a very difficult question to answer. So, once again, I will say to you, if the watch runs correctly and the spring is not broken, better leave it alone.

Many times, however, we are called upon to replace a broken mainspring in some popular model like the Hamilton we are using as a practice model. In this case it is a very simple matter to remove the broken spring and look up on your Hamilton chart the correct

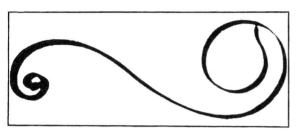

Illustration 74—Reverse Motor Barrel Mainspring. This spring will not set after winding. Due to its high elastic reaction it may be close to the elastic limit or breaking point and if not homogeneous will break under the slightest change in physical conditions.

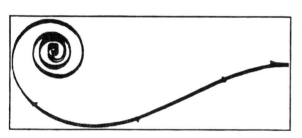

Illustration 75—Reverse Motor Barrel Mainspring after one year's service in a watch. Note how it has returned close to its original shape. This spring has a good elastic reaction but is close to its elastic limit or breaking point.

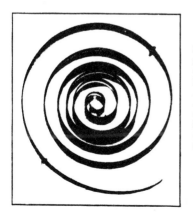

Illustration 76—This spring has a very poor elastic reaction. There is no danger of this spring breaking. It is too soft, however, to maintain an even motion, and is not suitable for good watch work. All springs of this kind should be changed and new ones fitted. Comparing the quality of a spring that breaks with that of one that sets, the one that breaks can be considered the better of the two springs.

spring for the 16s, 17 J grade, and by using the genuine Hamilton spring, it will fit perfectly. In which case all you need do is see that the ends are properly fitted into the slot in the barrel. Then oil the spring with a good grade watch oil. Perhaps a small drop is sufficient oil, if it is properly distributed around the spring.

However, there is more to it than that. First, we select the proper spring. Then we remove it from the wrapping and find that it is covered with a coating of grease to keep down rust. This grease may be removed by immersing in gasoline or a good cleaning fluid put up by the larger refineries. With a clean cloth then remove the liquid from the entire length of the spring.

Now select a barrel from your mainspring winder (See illustrations 15 to 18) that will slip free inside the watch barrel. Wind the spring first into the winder. Remove the winding arbor and you can see the spring just as it appears in the barrel. We next slip the winder into the barrel and work it around until the T end on the spring is fitted in the slot in the barrel. Hold it firmly there, and with the button on the winder, push the spring into the barrel, releasing the winder.

Examine it now to see that the inside coil is the proper size for the barrel arbor. It may have to be closed or opened. The arbor goes in so the hook on the arbor slips into the slot in the end of the spring. Now oil it. Then place the barrel in place; see first that the slot for the T end is in its proper position, and then press the head gently into barrel evenly all around. This may be done with a brush handle, or some other piece of wood or metal soft enough not to damage the barrel in any way.

Now grasp the protruding end of the barrel arbor with your tweezers or pliers and see that when it is turned forward that tension is brought to bear on it. In other words, see that it is catching the end of the spring.

Normally, the spring is now ready to go into the barrel and be wound for the first time. If there is no trouble, and you have not recently put a spring in this watch, perhaps all that is necessary is to wind it up and let it run.

Secret of Stopping Mainspring Breakage

Normally, the mainspring gives very little trouble. If it is correctly fitted and handled, there is little cause for worry about its performing as it should. But there is one thing that it will do — it will break. That is, if it is a good spring it will. Occasionally you will have a watch that seems prone to break springs. They will break for no apparent reason. Sometimes they will break during the first night they are in the watch. This often happens during a sharp change in atmospheric conditions, and if you examine one of these broken springs you will find that it is broken into several pieces.

No one knows exactly why springs break as they do. It is known that they break when the weather is extremely hot, or during a spring thunderstorm. They sometimes break for no reason at all. They simply break. Often two, three, or more will break in rapid succession in one watch.

There is a way to stop this, or to stop much of it. Keep this in mind for it is important. Not many watchmakers with experience know about it.

First, let it be understood that there is no definite way to keep a good spring from breaking. In fact, that it breaks occasionally proves that it is a GOOD spring. This may sound like double talk, but it is a fact. In order to understand it you must appreciate some fact about a piece of spring steel.

If the spring is soft — that is, does not have much resilience — it is not likely to break so easily. The sturdy, resilient spring is much more likely to break, also much more likely to pull the watch as it should be pulled. Therefore, the fact that it breaks means it is GOOD, rather than the other way around. The soft spring does not have the power needed. Thus it really causes more trouble than the good spring because it is not always easy to ascertain that a weak spring is the seat of the trouble. When a good spring breaks, you know immediately where the trouble lies and can go about correcting it.

If you follow the advice given below, you should have little trouble with breaking springs. In American springs always use Genuine. In Swiss watches, use the best spring you can buy, regardless of price. The cheap spring is more expensive in the long run. The C. & E. Marshall Company puts up a Swiss spring under their trade mark "Marco". It is one of the best springs obtainable at any price.

Let us assume that you have replaced a broken mainspring. After a few hours or a few days, the spring breaks again. Here is what to do:

First, be certain that you have selected the correct spring for that particular watch. Use a winder to put it in the barrel. Some watchmakers do not use a winder. Perhaps some can do as well with their hands, but I doubt it. So to protect yourself, use a winder always. After the spring is in the watch, oil it with a good grade of watch oil. Then wind it up and slowly release it several times.

Occasionally, the spring will break while you are doing this. So much the better if it does. You can then replace it while the watch is down. And you may rest assured that it would have broken within a few hours anyway. This winding process gives the spring a chance to get worked into the barrel, and the oil a chance to work around the spring. The several windings are approximately equal to that many 24 hour running periods for the spring. Thus, six windings are the nearest thing to six days running time. If the spring stands up during that breaking in period, the chances are it will continue to run.

In most shops it is customary to guarantee the life of a spring for one year from the date it is first replaced. So you can see that it becomes an expensive process if, because of continued breakage, it has to be replaced several times during the twelve-month period.

Wrist Watch Mainspring Work

We have covered the mainspring for the 16 size Hamilton very thoroughly. However, it is a simple spring and causes little trouble if the genuine spring is used at all times. In quite a few Swiss bracelet watches, however, fitting the proper spring is not quite so simple. And do not overlook the fact that a big majority of all watches in use today are bracelet and wrist watches.

Perhaps you have just repaired a wrist watch. You poised the balance, checked the escapement, and know that everything is in order. Yet the watch varies in positions.

The trouble may very well be in the mainspring. When you have traced the trouble to the mainspring, take it out of the barrel and lay it on the bench. If it straightens out like a new spring, it is either all right, or else it is not the correct spring for that watch. If it remains in a semi-wound state, it is set and should be replaced with a new one.

In either case, if you do not have a chart showing the correct size spring used by the manufacturer, you must use your own good judgment in selecting a replacement. There is a definite way of doing this.

In measuring mainsprings, there are two sets of gauges in popular use. One is known as the Dennison system. It is obsolete, inaccurate, and completely unsatisfactory.

The other is accurate to within $1/100$mm. This is the millimeter gauge. (See illustrations 77 to 81) It is a simple gauge that opens by turning the handle counterclockwise. The revolving cylinder is numbered from 0 to 50. Each number represents $1/100$mm. Thus one complete turn of the cylinder equals one-half millimeter. Two complete turns will equal $100/100$ mm or one complete millimeter.

The sleeve immediately under the cylinder is lined off in lines exactly 1 millimeter apart, from 0 to 15. Each one of these lines represents two complete turns of the cylinder, or one mm. This enables you

Adjustable Table for Measuring Jewels and Flat Parts.

Ground and Lapped to Precision Accuracy.

CHROME

PLATED

Ratchet Stop.

One Full turn of barrel equals one millimeter.

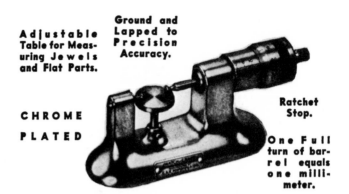

Illustration 77—Metric micrometer gauge designed and built especially for watchmakers. The first requisite for doing any kind of work is proper tools and this one is among the most necessary. The bench style heavy base prevents upsetting and permits operation of spindle with greatest ease and sensitivity—both hands being free.

Illustration 78—How gauge determines the diameter of wheels, jewels, cap jewels, settings, roller tables, pinion teeth, teeth of wheels, etc.

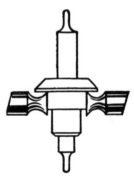

Illustration 80 — Measuring pivots or shoulders of staffs, pinions, stems, or any special measurement.

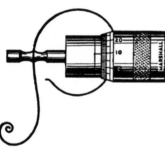

Illustration 79 — Measuring strength of mainspring on micrometer guage. Reading is 10/100 M.M. (Ten one hundredths of one Millimeter).

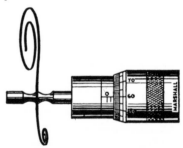

Illustration 81—Measuring width of mainspring. Reading is 1.60 M.M. (One and sixty one hundredths of Millimeter).

to read the gauge in millimeter and fractions thereof without confusion.

So, when measuring the spring we first open the gauge wide enough to slip the spring into the jaws edgewise. That is, to measure its width. To hold the spring level, place two coils between the jaws and close the gauge with the ratchet end until it stops and the ratchet begins working.

Now take your reading. Perhaps the base will read one millimeter plus 20 lines on the cylinder. If so, the spring is '1.20mm wide. On the chart and the envelope holding the spring this will be written 120. Correctly speaking it is 1mm and 20/100mm.

Remember that number, and now release the spring and measure its thickness. Perhaps this will be just 7/100mm. Thus we have a spring which measures 120 x 7. Now to get the length. The best way to do this is measure it in inches. For example, let us say it is 9½ inches long. If so, the numbers on the envelope will be 120 x 7 x 9½". Some manufacturers list the lengths in millimeters. If you wish to convert the length shown in millimeters to inches, simply multiply by 10 and divide the result by 254. That will give the length in inches.

We have now measured the spring which was in the watch. However, in the absence of a chart showing the correct spring for that particular model watch, we have no way of knowing whether the last man to replace the spring did so with the correct size. Here experience is a great asset. But since we cannot have experience until we get it, we will have to devise some method of checking the measurements.

Therefore, it is well to look at the spring carefully before removing it from the barrel. Observe if it looked to be the right length. That is, did not fill the barrel too full, and did fill it sufficiently full. If you are satisfied the length is correct, you pass on to the other measurements.

Since we took the spring out originally because we thought it was not strong enough, we reason that strength 7 is not enough for that particular watch. While the spring is in the barrel, we can also ascertain if the width is correct, by noting if it comes flush with the shoulder holding the barrel head. If it reached above this shoulder, then it is too wide and will not be free when the barrel head is in place. If it does not quite reach this shoulder, then it probably is the correct width.

By reasoning thus we find that we need a spring that measures one or two strengths stronger. Let us begin by selecting one that measures 120 x 9 x 9½.

In the absence of any spring at all — which is sometimes the case when the watch has been left in certain shops for repairs — we must have a way of locating the correct spring. Obviously this is not easy.

To begin, replace the barrel head in the barrel, leaving out the arbor. Using your millimeter gauge, measure the entire thickness of the barrel and head. Write the number down, thus — 200mm. Now remove the barrel head and measure its thickness, thus — 20mm. Measure the bottom of the barrel in the same manner — 20mm. We now subtract 20 plus 20mm or 40mm from 200mm, leaving us 160mm. Now allow approximately 10/100 millimeters for freedom sake and allow for error, and we find the spring should be approximately 150 millimeters wide. Since there is no way to determine the correct thickness in this manner, we can only guess at what we think it should be and fall back on the old method of trial and error. A little experience with this sort of thing will enable you to guess the correct strength in most cases.

There is a long process by which measurements may be made of the barrel and the exact spring determined. But this is so seldom necessary that it isn't worth your while to learn it.

Observe now that the wrist watches of almost all Swiss models have a mainspring somewhat different in construction from American watches. The Swiss use the hook end. Notice how the end fits into a notch cut into the side of the barrel.

Before inserting this spring, take a pair of flat nose pliers and grasp the end of the spring over the rivet holding the end in place. With a pair of heavy tweezers, raise the end of the hook approximately 1/16 inch away from the spring.

We now have a stronger spring than the one which we removed. Take off the packing grease in the usual way and put it in and wind it up. If the watch takes a quick springy motion — what is termed a good motion, or excellent motion — we know the spring is sufficiently strong. Now arises the possibility it is too strong.

You can ascertain if the spring is too strong by observing if it is rebanking. No, you do not yet know the meaning of that word, or the condition. Let me explain briefly: When a watch is taking the proper motion, the balance wheel swings in an arc of nearly 360 degrees. In the absence of a timing machine which will be discussed later in this series of lessons, you can best observe the motion of a watch by observing the roller jewel back of the balance when the watch is in motion. Almost directly back of the staff, the balance will stop its swing in one direction, and begin its swing in the other. The roller jewel may be observed at the exact instant of inertia. It then makes a complete circle the other way, and again stops in the same position and begins its return. Now this is as it should be. However, if it continues its swing well past the 360 degree arc, the roller jewel will strike the pallet fork on the opposite side. This may be hard to detect with the eye, but it may eaisly be heard by placing the watch against the ear. Instead of the usual "tick" and "tock", there will be a kind of double "tick" and double "tock". If the condition is very bad, it will sound somewhat like a horse's hoofs when he is galloping.

This is called rebanking. When the condition exists, the mainspring is too strong and the watch will gain several minutes over a twenty-four hour period. The only satisfactory solution is to replace the spring with a weaker one.

The spring we chose was strength 9; just two points stronger than the one we took out. If the watch rebanked, we know that two points is too much. Now, select a spring with exact measurements except it should be strength 8. If a weak spring was the real cause of the poor motion, the strength 8 should be correct.

If the watch does not rebank, yet has a lively motion, we must assume the spring is correct.

Fitting a Mainspring Properly

Occasionally you will have to fit a spring in a hurry and will not have the correct size on hand. In such a situation, you must be able to alter a spring to your needs. This is not difficult if you will follow a few simple rules.

First, of course ascertain the size spring needed. Then select from the available stock, one with correct thickness and width, but too long. Thickness and width cannot be altered. Measure off the correct number of inches, allow approximately one half inch, and break off the outside end of the spring.

If it is a very high class job, you may punch a hole in the end and rivet on a hook just as the factory spring is finished. Use a flat end punch on your stake or bench block to punch the hole. Now rivet a short end just as the factory does.

However, for practical purposes, there is a faster way. Using your small alcohol lamp for heat, grasp the end of the spring in a pair of flat nose pliers and let the flame contact the spring approximately one half inch back of the end. When the spring is a cherry red, fold the short end back as far as possible. Now hold the spring in the flame with the left hand, and with the right hand close the pliers down over the loop until the short end is laying neatly alongside the spring and the circumference of the loop is reduced to a minimum. We now have approximately one half inch of spring turned back. Take a small screw head file and file this end completely across about one eighth inch from the end of the spring.

Now break from the discarded piece of original spring a piece of spring approximately one half inch long and insert one end in the loop created in the flame. This you will observe gives you a nice hook that should catch snugly into the barrel. Here, too, a little experience will enable you to do a smooth job that will never fail to catch.

Repairing Swiss-Type Winding Unit

We cannot overlook the importance of the winding parts, including the following items. Crown, stem, clutch pinion, winding pinion, set lever, set lever screw, clutch spring, etc.

In previous lessons we have been working with the 16s Hamilton watch. This watch was chosen because of its size and ease of repairing. It is large enough for the inexperienced hands to handle with a reasonable amount of safety. Other watches vary not in principle, but only in application.

Now that we come to the study of the setting apparatus, I think it is time we leave the Hamilton for a while and give some thought to the Swiss watch. The Hamilton setting is so simple and sturdy and gives so little cause for repairs, the study of it is hardly worth while.

Now we will take up the wrist watch setting. Most American made small watches have what is known as the Swiss type setting. In short, the American watch manufacturers rather belatedly discovered that their system of stem and sleeve in the case was obsolete and not half so practical as the type apparatus used by the Swiss manufacturers. Being smart craftsmen, they have gradually changed over until almost all watches smaller than 3/0s now use the Swiss type stem.

The Swiss setting apparatus consists of stem, set screw, set lever, clutch pinion, clutch lever, clutch spring, and setting bridge. (See illustration 70) This setting bridge is the only part of the watch that can be patented. The principle of time keeping not being patentable. Therefore, this setting bridge, clutch lever, and set lever constitutes the key to Swiss watch material.

To find the material needed, compare the three items mentioned above with the swiss watch chart furnished by your Jewelers Supply house. Use first a ligne gauge to determine the size of the watch, as the Swiss people use the ligne system of measurements. It has no exact comparison in American systems of measurement.

To determine the correct size, measure the movement diameter at the stem. Then compare setting bridges listed under this size until you find the illustration exactly like the watch to be repaired. Then simply order whatever part wanted, giving the series number on the illustration. This being the key to watch material, the part ordered should fit almost perfectly.

On such well known watches as Bulova and Gruen, all parts may be ordered by giving the number on the watch; such as, 10AN or 6AE,

GENUINE FACTORY WATCH PARTS

Illustration 82—Swiss watch material system. The correct part is always at your finger tips. Two top drawers of cabinet contain little boxes with illustrated lids and description of contents. System starts with 144 boxes holding 2016 parts, leaving 6 empty drawers for other watch materials. Improves the efficiency of any shop by eliminating many miscellaneous boxes and cabinets, replacing them with a single compact unit in which all parts can be found instantly.

or whatever the number of the Bulova may be. The Gruen uses a series of numbers starting about 100 and running up to nearly one thousand. By demanding Genuine Bulova or Genuine Gruen material at all times, you are certain of getting parts that fit with a minimum of fitting.

Almost all men's Bulova watches are now made in America. But they are made on machines imported from Switzerland, and to all intents and purposes are still Swiss watches. Even though they are marked "made in U. S. A.", the material is found in the same manner as Swiss watches. Incidentally, it is one of the easiest watches to repair.

Most supply houses have some system of their own for supplying material for all Swiss watches. (See illustration 82) In these systems you will also find material for both Gruen and Bulova watches. If genuine material is not available, perhaps that listed in your regular Swiss system will answer your purpose adequately.

Now that we know something about the how and wherefores of the Swiss watch, let us go into some detail regarding the stem and setting apparatus.

Swiss Setting Apparatus Methods

There is no need of going into long paragraphs regarding some parts of a watch unless we actually have these parts before us as we go. So, the next thing to do is get some good 10½ ligne Swiss movements. If possible to obtain, get a Bulova 10AN or 10AX or any other Bulova in the 10½ ligne size.

Just a word of caution here about taking these movements from the cases. Often inexperienced people damage a watch in trying to get the movement out of the case. Some of the older watches used three piece cases and the movements were held in the case just as pocket sizes. Modern models, however, are placed in one piece cases and the movement simply lifts out.

Having nothing to hold them securely in the case except friction, they naturally fit the case much closer than other models, thus making a few accidents unavoidable. If certain precautions are used, however, damage may be avoided and a lot of time and grief will be avoided at the same time.

Use a good case opener to open the end of the case. Then the movement is lifted upward. Perhaps the series of photographs (illustrations 83, 84, and 85) will tell better than words just how best to extricate a movement from the modern case. As the photographs illustrate, due to the proximity of the balance wheel to the case opening there is great danger of breaking a staff or bending a pivot if extreme care is not used.

Now to get back to the subject of this lesson, the Swiss setting apparatus. It differs from the American type in many ways and particulars. Many large American watches still use the now obsolete sleeve. This is not practical for the smaller watches. In fact, it is no practical for the larger ones, either. Slowly the American manufacturers are coming around to that realization.

In the Swiss watches that still use the three piece cases and the two piece waterproof cases, there is still another problem. These movements do not just lift out. They, too, use case screws, but after the screws are removed, the stem must be taken out by letting up a round or two on the small set lever screw up beside where the stem goes into the movement. In the old days, this screw was called a "detent screw" or "detention screw". Now it is generally known as a set

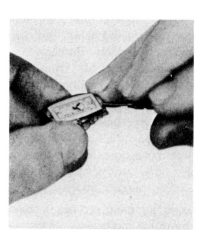

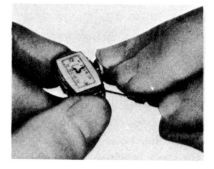

Illustrations 83, 84, 85—Most modern watch movements fit tightly in one-piece cases. This simplifies your work but makes it necessary that you use extreme caution to avoid damage to staff or pivot in removal.

screw. Its function is to hold the set lever into the groove of the stem.

To release it more than a round and a half or two rounds, will cause the screw to come completely out of the set lever. Therefore, to avoid trouble release the set screw just enough to permit the stem to be pulled out of the movement. Then remove the case screws and the movement will slip easily from the case.

Considerable stress is being placed on removing bracelet movements from their cases. There is a definite reason for this. That reason is the protection of the balance. Look out for the balance at all times. In doing any kind of repairs to a watch, always remove the balance assembly as quickly as possible. It is very important and rather delicate. It is easily broken, especially when handled with only partially trained hands. By removing it first, you avoid costly and embarrassing accidents. Especially is this true when you are learning, as accidents are more likely to happen before your hands and eyes are properly trained in the handling of small parts.

Assuming that you are going to replace a broken stem, we now have the movement out of the case. Next remove the hands and dial. Many times, the dial too is held in a different manner. Perhaps it is held by two screws going through the plate from the front. They have half heads, and must be turned half way around to release the dial feet.

With the dial off, the entire stem assembly is before you. If it is one of the better or more popular makes such as Bulova or Gruen, a new stem is found by the number as explained in a previous lesson. Usually all that is necessary in a watch of this kind is to find the correct stem, oil the arbor (the square) just a little, cut the thread end off to the right length, and fit a crown. No other fitting is necessary.

If it is not one of the well known makes, the fitting process is somewhat different. You first ascertain the size of the movement. Then we compare the setting apparatus with your Swiss chart until you find the exact setting apparatus on the chart. All three parts must be the same — that is, the setting bridge, set lever, and clutch lever. Also the ligne size of the watch must be that of the illustration shown. Then the number shown on the chart will usually supply the correct stem. (See illustration 82)

If however, the correct stem is not available and is not obtainable, there is just one way out — make it. This is not nearly so difficult as it sounds. Even if there is no sample available, you can still make a stem that will fit perfectly.

Assuming you have a sample, the end of the old stem or at least the arbor to guide you, you may easily determine the size of stem wanted. First, use the millimeter gauge to find the diameter of the stem at the hub. Then select from your stock of Stubs steel wire a piece of steel just this size, if possible. Should you not have the exact size, select the next largest size and cut it down to the desired size. Thus you have the hub correct before you actually start the stem.

Chuck the wire into the lathe, leaving enough end protruding to complete the entire stem without having to remove the wire from the lathe until it is finished. If the wire does not immediately spin true, true it before tightening the chuck.

See that your cutting graver is sharp and has a smooth cutting edge. Begin by cutting the pilot. That is the small point of the stem that proceeds it into the movement and holds it in place. Hence, the name, pilot. If you have a good sample, cut this pilot to the exact size and length of the sample, using the sample as a gauge as to length. Use your millimeter gauge to determine the correct size. (Learn to use the millimeter gauge by holding it in the palm of the right hand while turning the ratchet with the thumb and fingers of that hand. Then the reading will face you at all times.)

When the pilot is finished, lay the old stem against the blank in the lathe and use the small point of your graver to make a small ring

Illustrations 86, 87—Flat gravers for block lettering, old English solid cutting and wriggling.

around the blank indicating the length of the arbor. Let another mark indicate the width of the winding pinion shoulder. Back of that make two other marks to indicate the position and width of the groove.

It is a simple matter to do this by holding the old stem against the blank in your lathe. Hold the stem by the thread end and make your measurements in reverse order — that is, with the two stems facing each other.

Now use your millimeter gauge to determine the size of the stem where the winding pinion goes. This diameter will be the next step to cut to. Here you cut from the second mark back of the pilot. Cut the stem evenly and smoothly. Keep cutting them over and over until you can turn out a perfect job. The easiest way is to turn the lathe at a fairly fast rate of speed. When the whole length of this cutting is finished to the correct size, you are ready to cut the square. (Make all shoulders sharp, just like the factory stems.)

Before starting the square, slip the winding pinion over the stem to see that it fits. It should be free, but snug. Slip the pinion on backwards — that is, the beveled teeth should face the lathe now. The back of the pinion should be toward the pilot of the stem. You will see why very quickly now.

On the back of the lathe head is an index. It contains a series of holes, numbered from 1 to 60. Also the quarters are indicated, such as 0 —— 15 —— 30, and back to 0 again. These numbers being one-fourth way around the head, for perfect squares. Use the plunger to lock the lathe on zero.

Now use a six inch flat file, cut three or four. Keep the uncut edge of the file next to the back of the pinion which you left on the stem thus. With smooth, even strokes across the steel, cut a flat side from the pinion to the pilot.

Do not try to finish each side as you go along. Rather, hit it a few even strokes, seeing that the cutting is smooth and flat, then turn the lathe to number 15 and lock again.

Following this process, turn to number 30 on the lathe index, and so on until the square is complete. When you have finished the fourth side, it should be approximately correct for the clutch pinion. Try it by slipping the clutch over the square. If it is not small enough, repeat the above process with a finer file and try the clutch after each operation. When the clutch slides easily over the square, or arbor, it is time to stop.

The square is not finished, but it is time to pass on to the next operation. If you marked your blank correctly, you have a space outlined for the groove. This is cut with a small flat end graver. (See illustrations 86 and 87) When the groove is the right width and depth, you are ready to cut the threads.

Again use your old stem as a gauge for the length of the hub. Then release the stem and pull it out far enough to allow for the threads. Then with the point of the graver cut the blank completely off at that point.

Reverse the stem in the chuck, inserting it down to the end of mark indicating the beginning of the hub. That is where the threads must stop. Again use your millimeter gauge to determine the size of thread you want, and cut the stem down to that size just as you cut the other end before filing the square. When you have reached the correct size, oil that number in your screw plate and cut the thread. (See illustration 88)

This is done by holding the screw plate flat against the stem and gently screwing the stem into it. Keep it oiled so it will cut freely. If it seems too tight, work it back and forth gently, bringing it a little more forward than backward each time.

With the threads finished, we must now finish the stem. If your cutting and filing have been up to par — and keep it up until they are — there is little to do except polish. Remember, that this stem will quite likely come into the hands of other workmen, and they are inclined to be quite critical. So for that reason if for no other, you want to do your very best job. Make it look exactly like a factory stem. With a little experience and effort you can do it. The first few will be very bad. After that you will see an improvement with each one. Do not be satisfied to go on to the next lesson until you can make a perfect stem.

You have no one to examine your work and criticise it. No one but yourself to tell you how bad or how good it is. You would not, as critic, permit yourself, as workman, to get by with anything shoddy, would you?

A very good way to finish the stem is to grasp the thread in a linvise. Take an emery stick and go over the round surfaces and then the square. Follow this with a fine cut emery buff to remove the marks left by the rough buff. A high polish is really not necessary here.

The stem is now ready for use. If it is a pocket watch, perhaps the steel should have a little hardening. For the average bracelet watch, hardening is not necessary.

Steel Tempering Made Easy

Tempering steel is not a difficult process. Although it is not strictly a part of this series of lessons, it will be covered here only because certain instructions are believed necessary. And information gained in this lesson may be used throughout your life to good advantage when working with steel. If you are interested in learning more about this subject, books can be had treating it in great detail. Here, we shall confine ourselves to the bare essentials.

There are many ways of tempering steel, just as there are many grades of steel itself. If the stem is a small one as are so often used in large watches, it should be tempered.

The first process is heating.

Place it on a small flat piece of copper or silver, or even a charcoal block. Play a gas or alcohol flame over it until the entire stem becomes a cherry red. Then quickly dump it into a glass of water. It must reach the water while it is still red.

When it comes out of the water it is hard, so hard, in fact, that it would probably break before winding the watch the first time. Therefore, you now proceed to temper it. That is, you draw it to the desired degree of hardness.

The first process now is to polish the stem very bright.

Then gently pass it back and forth through a small flame until it turns a bright straw color. This color leaves it hard and strong. Even if it should become a light purple, that is not so bad. It is a little softer than the straw color, but not too soft. After the stem is polished again, it is ready to go into the watch.

In the case of several very fine Swiss made watches, rather large stems with very small arbors (squares) are used. Many times these stems break easily, and replacements break just as easily. Often this forces one to do some experimenting with steel tempering in order to find a stem that will not break in ordinary use.

Some temper in oil; some in beeswax; some use soap, and many other agents. Perhaps one of the least known of the better tempering agents is a raw Irish potato.

Split the potato open. Heat the stem to a deep cherry red, and quickly insert it between the halves of the potato and close them over it. Let it remain there until completely cold. For some reason which perhaps you understand, if you know chemistry, this Irish potato juice gives steel great tensil strength.

Illustration 88—Bracelet size screw plate. Double notched.

Fitting a Stem Without a Sample

Many watches come in for repairs without stems. Perhaps the stem has been lost. If so, and there is no genuine stem available for that particular model, you are faced with another problem — fitting a stem without a sample to go by.

It is not difficult. It does, however, require a little more working knowledge of your tools. For that reason, it is suggested that you fit several stems as suggested below.

Go about it just as in making a stem from a sample, with these exceptions: First remove the entire setting apparatus, including the set lever. Fit a blank wire to the opening in the movement itself. If it fits snugly without being reduced, so much the better. Chuck it in the lathe just as before and cut the pilot. You can tell when the pilot is small enough by fitting it in the watch.

When the pilot is correct, slip the movement over the blank in the lathe until the pilot goes into place. Hold the movement there with one hand and hold the graver with the other as you let the lathe revolve slowly; and with the point of the graver held where the set lever comes normally, make a mark on the stem. Let a similar mark indicate the position of the end of the arbor. Another two marks or circles on the blank should indicate the position of the groove. Each of these last two marks should be on either side of the set lever when it is in position. In this manner, you simply lay a pattern on your blank, then proceed to cut the stem to your pattern.

When all positions are indicated, remove the movement and begin cutting just as before. Again you use the winding pinion backwards to act as a stop in filing the arbor.

So you see it is possible to make a perfect stem without actually knowing a single dimension before hand.

Occasionally, too, you will find a watch that has had an improperly fitted stem at some previous date, and the plates have worn egg shaped around the stem. Many times the plates have been cut out by a roughly finished stem, or rather, by a stem that was not finished at all. Many times you will find the plates so worn that the genuine stem will not fit. Perhaps the oversize model is still too small. Then you should know how to proceed.

A very good way to begin is to remove the complete setting apparatus, but leave the plates just as they should be. Use a reamer to round up the stem hole and see that the edges are smooth and parallel. Now make and fit the stem in the usual manner, and you will find that you have an oversized stem that really fits as snug and works as well as when the watch was new.

In doing any job of this kind, don't overlook the important fact that considerable experience and skill are required to do a first class job. And we are interested in no other.

Correcting Set Lever Trouble

In the Swiss watch where the stem is used quite a lot, there are several points of wear. Therefore, there are several points of friction which demand correct oiling. If they are not correctly oiled and kept clean and kept properly oiled, unusual wear often results. As a direct result of improper care or improper repair, is the set lever which will no longer tighten down enough to hold the stem securely.

Here we have a trouble that should be corrected before it becomes too serious. Yet, unless you have the genuine set screw and set lever, it is a hard one to correct. By all means obtain the genuine material and replace all worn setting parts if possible.

If you cannot possibly obtain the proper set screw, then an alteration is called for. There are two or three things that can correct it. One of the most likely causes is the screw being too long. Even when it is screwed down tight, it does not hold the set lever snugly in the groove of the stem.

If this is the case, here is how to correct it. Remove the set screw, chuck it up in the lathe and remove just enough of the shoulder that stops the set lever, to permit the lever to come up flush with the plate.

Try the screw in its proper place in the plate. When shoulder is cut down to the proper depth, take your screw plate and cut threads up to the shoulder. If this is properly done, you will find that it then holds the set lever in correct position and the trouble is corrected.

Another less expensive method — also a less satisfactory one — is to place a small washer under the set screw shoulder on the main plate. This will have the effect of raising the entire screw and thus adjusting the set lever. This job is not recommended except in extreme emergencies, and then only as a last resort.

If there is no other way and there is no washer available, you can make one. Do this by selecting a piece of steel just the size of the large shoulder or hub of the set screw. Through this steel wire drill a hole that will accommodate the shoulder of the set screw. Then use a small saw or screw head file to cut off a washer the thickness desired. Polish and harden it. Put it on the plate and push the set screw through and then start the set lever on and tighten screw down.

This last method is suggested largely as home work. That is, it is the kind of work that teaches you to do many jobs with the lathe, drill, saw and files. Do it over and over many times until you can do it perfectly.

In starting to drill the hole, take a standard pivot drill and place in a pin vise. After using a very sharp turning graver to locate the center of the spinning steel in the lathe, start drilling a hole directly into the end of the steel with the drill. Hold the drill against it gently, occasionally dipping the drill in oil to keep it from getting hot. Oil also helps it to cut the steel. Try to drill a perfectly round hole of any size you want.

If you do not have the size drill you need, a drill may be easily made. It is done as follows:

Take a piece of steel the size you want. Using a good file, file each side down until it is almost flat at one end. That is, until both sides are flat. Then point it off to a center. Then cut the two back edges down until the cutting edges are sharp and clean like the cutting end of a graver.

Harden this drill, put a little oil on it and notice how well it cuts steel or other medium hard or soft metals of all kinds. Once you have learned to make a drill of this kind, you need never want for drills as long as you have a piece of steel.

If further instructions for making are necessary, take an old drill and shape yours as nearly like it as possible.

Staff-Fitting in Swiss Bracelet Watches

In a previous lesson we discussed the fitting of a staff to American watches in some detail. You used the larger size watch first, because of the need for you to improve the muscle coordination of the eye and hands before trying the smaller watch.

If you have faithfully completed every operation outlined in preceding lessons, then you are ready for the job at hand.

Take one of the movements which you used for fitting stems. Remove the balance assembly. Remove the dial and hands, so you will have access to both top and foot balance jewels.

The hairspring and roller table are removed in the usual manner. Now either cut away the hub as illustrated in an earlier lesson, or use a staff remover to take the staff out. For the sake of having a perfect sample, better knock this one out.

The K & D staff remover (See illustration 89) is very good for staff removing. Place the staff on the stake, tighten the remover over it so the balance arm will not be sprung with the pressure of moving the staff. Drive the staff out with one quick stroke. (See illustration 90)

Using your setting apparatus as a guide — you will remember it is the key to Swiss material — locate the model on which you happen to be working. When you have done this, get several staffs from your supply house for the series number. Push the staff into the block of pith in the usual manner and test the hub, the roller table, and the hairspring collet. They should fit almost as perfectly as did the Hamilton. If not, turn back to the past lessons and read once again the paragraphs on fitting — that is, if you do not remember. If you know what to do, proceed without re-reading instructions.

Fit the pivots to the jewels in the usual manner. However, here you will find one difference. The balance jewels are set directly in the plate. By removing two screws, the cap jewels or end stones come off, leaving the balance jewels stationary in their positions.

A good way to test the length of the staff is to measure the top end with the old staff, then the shank. If the hub is the same depth, it should be correct. To be sure of the length, leave the cap jewels off, but place the balance cock back in position and place the screw in it. Now use your guage to measure the depth of the watch from the back of one balance jewel to the back of the other. The staff must be no longer than this. The reason is obvious.

If the pivots must be fitted to the balance jewels, leave the balance cock on the plate as described above. Chuck the staff into the lathe, spin the pivots true by holding a hard piece of pegwood against the

Illustration 89—Staff Remover. Select the proper hole in your staking tool die, adjust the staff remover according to directions — strike punch a sharp blow with hammer and staff will be removed without injury to balance.

staff while the lathe is running and the staff is not too tight in the chuck. When it is true, tighten chuck sufficiently to hold it true.

With the balance cock on the plate you have access to each jewel so you can try the pivots from time to time as you polish them down. When you change ends with the staff, simply turn the watch over and use the other jewel.

After the pivots are small enough to go into the jewels from the back, polish in the usual manner and see that the ends are perfectly flat, with the corner just slightly rounded. That is, the pivot should be exactly as in Illustration 91. You will notice the end is flat, yet there are no sharp edges.

Now stake the staff into the wheel if you have not already done so. Do this just as you did the Hamilton staff. Now place the bottom cap jewel in place after properly oiling it. Then remove the balance cock and place the staff in the jewels and screw down the balance cock. Note carefully the height of the top pivot. Does it just come through the balance jewel? Place a straight edge over the jewel and notice if doing so moves the balance. In other words, does the pivot protrude. If so, it is just that much too long and must be polished down until it is flush with the balance jewel. Then when the cap jewel goes in position, there will be no binding of the pivots and no end shake.

How to Make Parts You Cannot Buy

With certain unusual and obsolete models of Swiss watches, material is not easily obtained. You will not encounter many of this type, but the occasional job must be handled. Furthermore, you want to be able to do any job that comes into the store. To do that you must be able to make a staff as well as a stem.

For the best results, staffs should be cut from tempered steel made especially for that purpose. When this is done, tempering is not necessary. But for the time being, you had better confine your efforts to stubs steel wire.

Select a wire large enough to cover the overall size of the sample staff. Chuck it into the lathe and permit enough to extend to fully cover the length of the staff. Now in doing the following staff cutting, you are going to work along somewhat the same lines as in making a stem, but here the work is much more precise.

You will use the old staff as a sample by which to guage the length of the new. But for other dimensions, you must measure the old staff. Begin by measuring the side of the collet shoulder, and write it down thus: Collet shoulder 55, balance shoulder 65, shank 40. These measurements are easily made with your millimeter guage just as you measured mainsprings with it. Each of the numbers listed above is that many 1/100mm.

The reason for writing these numbers down close at hand is to have quick reference to them. Then mark the steel with the point of the graver where the hub should be. That is, reverse the old staff which came out of the watch and hold the top part of it against the blank. Use the graver to indicate the position of each shoulder. When this is done, begin by cutting the collet shoulder. Then the small shoulder at the top of it, followed in turn by the top pivot. From there you go to the hub for the balance wheel.

Cut each of these shoulders to the sizes indicated by the measurements previously taken.

After you have finished the top half of the staff and have it down to proper dimensions, leave just enough space to take care of the hub and cut the roller table shank down to the approximate size. This shank cannot be finished until the staff has been cut off and reversed in the lathe.

Do that now and you will find that you have almost finished the entire staff before removing it from the original steel blank. It is best

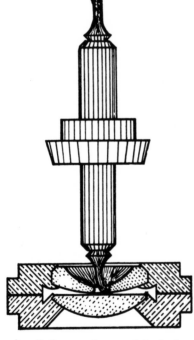

Illustration 90—Shows results of dropping or bumping a watch. The lower balance pivot is bent and the jewel is badly chipped. The top pivot is burred, the result of a slight bump. Staffs and jewels in this condition must be changed and new ones fitted.

to do all the work possible before cutting off the staff. You know that the staff is true before it is removed from the original blank, therefore, you have avoided errors in truing it.

But it is not yet finished. Before you may call it a finished staff, you must chuck it into another chuck and finish the roller table shank, and then bevel off the shoulder of the hub just as the original was beveled. The pivot may be finished down to almost the correct size with a sharp cutting graver.

The staff is now cut, and the finishing process begins. If it was cut from soft steel wire, it must be tempered. If you used a piece of tempered steel, there remains only to finish the pivots and put it in the watch. If it must be tempered, there is always the danger of getting it out of true in the process. Proceed as follows:

With every part of the staff except the pivots finished, you leave them rough and large until the tempering is finished. Before continuing, you must make a tool for the tempering job. Use a piece of silver wire and make a long loop on the end, leaving the loop just large enough to hold the staff securely. Then slip the staff into the loop, letting the shoulder rest on top of the silver wire loop.

Now play a small flame onto the silver wire until the heat thus conducted brings the staff to a cherry red. Immediately dump it into a container of water. This should leave it quite hard.

The next step is to polish the staff to a bright finish. Then place it back into the silver holder and pass this holder back and forth through a small flame from your lamp until it conducts sufficient heat to bring the staff to a deep straw color, or a light purple color, depending on how hard you want the staff to remain. Since the wheel shoulder should be a little softer than the other parts, this process will probably bring the hub to a blue color while bringing the pivots to a straw or light purple. That is correct.

After you have brought the temper to what your better judgment tells you it should be, polish the pivots down to fit the jewels just as previously instructed to polish pivots. Stake the staff into the balance wheel, place the lower cap jewel in position, and try the staff in the watch. By leaving the top cap jewel off during this fitting process, you can determine if the overall length is too much. If you cannot get it perfect in the first cutting, always leave it a little long. Then it is quite simple to cut it down to the proper length when you can try it in the watch and determine the exact amount of correction necessary.

It is suggested that you make several staffs. At first, do not try to be too accurate. Just turn out staffs until you can do a perfect job of turning. Then copy a few until your measurements are as perfect as the sample which you used.

This in invaluable experience. You may not have to make many complete staffs, but it is a big help to know how to alter one just slightly. You certainly should know how to make one should it ever be necessary.

The Best System of Fitting Crowns

The fitting of crowns is perhaps one of the most difficult small jobs the workman is called on to do. This is due to the fact that no definite standard has been established for crown diameters, thickness, thread sizes and the like.

The best suggestion is to buy the very best crown outfit that can be had if you have to fit many crowns. In the long run, the system will pay for itself many times over.

Perhaps here it is well to stress one of the things which you SHOULD NOT do. No doubt you have gone into a repair shop many times for a crown. The workman would remove the stem from the watch and take up a cigar box of crowns and scratch around through it like a setting hen looking for a worm, until he finally found something which could be used.

Illustration 91—Hamilton balance pivot.

If it were a large store where a lot of work was done, he perhaps had several hundred dollars tied up in crowns alone. Yet, to fit a small crown, he spent two or three times the necessary time in looking for something that could be used.

Get the idea now that time is money; today time is valuable and should be saved. Furthermore, in addition to time saving, you are more likely to find what you want if you have it where it can be seen. Take our man described above looking for a crown. Suppose he had only a half dozen crowns in the lot that would fit the stem in question; chances are ten to one he could never find them. So in crowns, as in everything else, keep them in order. Known where to put your hands on what you want instantly. It pays.

Even with the best of crown systems, crowns still remain a problem. Here we are going to treat largely with bracelet crowns because they constitute about 99½ per cent of all crowns fitted today.

The better crown cabinets (See illustrations 92 to 97) contain several styles and sizes of crowns in all colors. You will notice that they also contain a guage for tap sizes. Tap size refers to the thread size. First, select from your chart the proper color of gold and the proper diameter of crown. Then, if you have the tap size needed, all you have to do is screw the crown on tightly enough to turn the hands backward or forward.

Illustration 92—Crown system that makes 228 crowns fit thousands of cases and movements. Pick out crown that matches case; it is a simple matter to make any thread size required for the stem (see illustrations 93 to 97).

If you do not have the tap size to fit the stem in question, use the guage to ascertain the tap size wanted. Then place the crown in the crown holder. (See illustration 98) Then ream the pipe of the crown with the reamer using the correct corresponding number. Then use the thread cutter of the same number and rethread the crown. That is all there is to it. And to fit one correctly takes only a few minutes, if

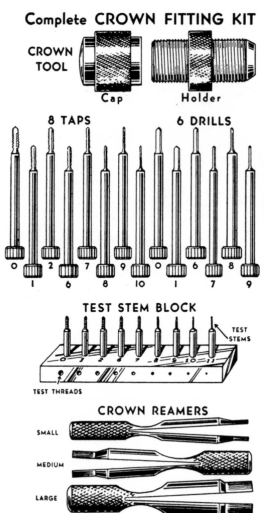

Illustration 93—Crown tools for taking care of every shape and size for all Swiss and American watches. With this system you can fit a crown to any case, without ordering crowns of various thread sizes.

you have the assortment arranged so you can quickly find what you want.

Occasionally you will find a crown that will not stay on the stem. When the watch is set backward, the crown screws off. There are

Illustrations 94 to 97—How to use crown fitting tools. Use flat end of holder for pocket watch crowns. Use beveled end of holder when rethreading wrist watch crowns.

1. Select crown that matches case. Insert tap No. 10 through holder. Screw crown onto end of tap.

2. Screw cap tight onto holder. Crown is now perfectly centered for reaming and rethreading.

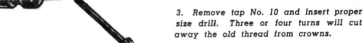

3. Remove tap No. 10 and insert proper size drill. Three or four turns will cut away the old thread from crowns.

4. Remove drill and insert tap of size needed. A few turns of the tap will cut a thread deep enough for the stem to fit perfectly. That's all there is to it. Your crown is now ready for use.

several ways of correcting this when no other crown is available. All of them are bad. Sometimes they must be resorted to.

One of the most satisfactory is to place a small piece of soft solder in the pipe of the crown. First clean stem and crown, of course. Just a drop of soldering acid on the solder, and screw to stem into the desired position. Then hold the stem over a small alcohol flame just long enough to flow the solder. This will make the crown secure, and does no real injury to either crown or stem.

As in any soldering job, however, the acid must be removed when the job is finished. A very good way to clean a solder job is to immerse it in a cyanide solution and then boil with baking soda. Then clean and dry in the usual way.

Illustration 98—Crown Tools. Carry in stock crowns of only the most popular Tap (Thread) sizes. If an odd size should be needed, a crown can be rethreaded in a few minutes time.

American Stem and Sleeve Methods

Nearly all American pocket watches still use the old fashioned sleeve. This is a very unsatisfactory setting apparatus, unless the watch is a high grade one using a set lever such as the 16s Hamilton. Most cheap watches do not have set levers.

With these models, setting is done by pulling up on the crown until the stem slides up one notch in the spring sleeve. There are as many different size sleeves and stems as there are watches to use them. These sleeves frequently have to be replaced.

First, remove the crown. With a sleeve wrench, screw the sleeve out of the case. Select a new sleeve the exact size and length of the old one. See that the sleeve fits the shoulder of the stem quite snugly. When you are convinced that you have the correct sleeve, place a small amount of oil or heavy cup grease on the working shoulder and screw the sleeve into the case.

In order for the setting to work properly, the stem is to reach just a given depth and no more or less. It may be necessary to adjust the depth several times before getting it just right.

Remember, too, that the stem must fit the sleeve snugly enough to hold the setting apparatus in winding position against the upward pressure of the setting spring.

Fitting the Cannon Pinion, Hands, etc.

We now come to that very important part of the watch, the hands. Perhaps in other instances we have stressed the fact that some particular part was so important that everything else about the watch could be perfect, and yet it would not function properly if this particular part were incorrect. That is so true it will bear repetition. It is also true of the hands.

The hands proper, and their study, must of necessity include the cannon pinion, minute wheel, hour wheel, and inter-setting wheels. A small book could be written about this one section of the watch. However, we are going to try to give you the fundamentals as briefly as possible. We are going to give them to you in a practical way that will be easily understood, if you actually do the work as you go along.

For this work I think it well to go back to the 16s Hamilton with which we started originally. This particular part of almost all watches is the same. And what we want now is to learn the principle on which it works.

First, after removing the hands and dial, you find there are the following parts: hour wheel, which is the large wheel that fits over and around the cannon pinion. It is called the hour wheel for obvious reasons. The cannon pinion is also so named because of its position being similar to a cannon. Next comes the minute wheel, which lies next to the plate and meshes with the cannon pinion. The inter-setting wheels are the small wheels between the minute wheel and the setting clutch.

Without getting involved in too many technicalities, let's give these wheels and their functions just a little study.

The minute hand fits over the cannon pinion. The hour hand fits over the hour wheel. We know that when the minute hand makes one complete turn of the dial, the hour hand must travel just one twelfth as far. Of course the minute hand makes exactly the same number of revolutions as the center wheel, but that does not concern the point in question now.

We know, also, that in order for the cannon pinion (which carries the minute hand) to travel just exactly twelve times as fast as the hour wheel (which carries the hour hand) there must be a definite system of gears worked out to the fraction of a second. This is all done with the cannon pinion, the hour wheel, and the minute wheel. It is not nearly so complicated as it seems.

It is worked out on a three-four basis; that is, if the cannon pinion has 9 teeth, the minute wheel must have 27 teeth, or three times as many as the cannon pinion. Likewise, the minute wheel pinion would have 8 teeth and the hour wheel 32, or just four times as many. The number of teeth given here are used merely as an illustration. They vary in different watches. The cannon pinion may have eight teeth and the minute wheel 24. In that case, the minute wheel pinion would have 7 teeth and the hour wheel 28.

Thus we see that there are certain definite, dependable laws governing the watch in all its parts. If you should lose a minute wheel, how would you go about replacing it, provided the factory model was not available? That is simple. Count the teeth of the cannon pinion, and then the teeth of the hour wheel. If the cannon pinion has 9 teeth, the minute wheel should have 27. If the hour wheel has 32 teeth, the minute wheel pinion must have 8. If the rotation is in reverse order, then it would be the other way around, for only on this basis can we arrive at the correct number of revolutions for each one.

You were told in one of the first lessons that every part of a watch with friction should be oiled. That is true. But there are certain parts that may appear to have friction, but actually have very little. One of these is the minute wheel. Place absolutely no oil under this wheel or on its bearing.

Hour, Minute and Inter-Setting Wheels

If you doubt the wisdom of the above statement, try putting a drop of oil under the minute wheel of an otherwise clean, well running watch. Watch how quickly it stops. For there is no real friction here and a drop of oil on this flat surface forms a vacuum. You have noticed this if you have ever taken down a watch which has been drowned in oil. You found the minute wheel hard to remove. First, one side had to be raised to break the vacuum.

Likewise, there should be no oil placed on or in the hour wheel pipe. It must move smoothly and freely over the cannon pinion. Many times after bracelet watches have been cleaned, the hour wheel binds on the canon pinion. This will cause the watch to stop. If it does not stop, it will run irregularly. Therefore, one of the first things to check when assembling a watch is the hour wheel. Is it free on the cannon pinion? If it binds just a little, a good way to correct it is to use a large cutting broach and insert it in the wheel and turn just a round or two, change ends with the wheel, and repeat the performance. This should be sufficient. Try it again and when the hour wheel is free, stop.

Another thing to check is the height of the hour wheel pipe. Does it come above the hand shoulder of the cannon pinion? In the old days this trouble was quite prevalent. Today one seldom finds this condition unless some part has been improperly fitted. But to be safe, check the hour wheel pipe. If it does come above flush with the minute hand seat on the pinion, dress the end of the pipe down with a hand emery buff, being sure to do it evenly and smoothly across. When this is done, the hour wheel should fit freely over the pinion with a minimum of tolerance either way.

Getting the Cannon Pinion Just Right

With new watches, the cannon pinion gives very little trouble. Usually you can proceed just as if it had been tested and found perfect. However, if one is to be replaced or if the watch is an old one, you may expect trouble and the chances are you will not be kept waiting.

When you have cleaned a watch, always place just a little oil under the cannon pinion, pull the stem to setting position and try moving the pinion around gently. If it is oiled, you can easily see if it is too loose. The cannon pinion should be just tight enough to carry the hands without slipping, and no tighter.

You will encounter many watches with pinions so tight they are very hard to set. This is a mistake. There is no real need of the cannon pinion being that tight. It has only to carry the hands. However, it must be tight enough in every position that it will not permit the watch to run without the hands moving. By examining a few new watches and giving the problem some thought, you will be able to tell when the pinion is just right.

When a pinion must be tightened, operate as follows:

Remove the pinion from the watch. Notice it has a grooved waist line. Observe this with your loupe and you will see that it has been forced inward on either side. This recess is matched on the center post with a corresponding groove. One works in the other to hold the pinion down so it cannot work upward while being turned. It also holds it tight to the center post. / Here, then, is where it must be tightened.

Catch the waist of the pinion in a pair of cutting pliers or tweezers. (See illustration 99) Hold the pinion just tightly enough with the jaws of the pliers that it cannot drop out. Then with a light hammer handle or some other light piece of wood, tap the back of the pliers once or twice just enough to force the waist of the barrel inward. Stop and try it occasionally so you will not over do the thing.

If the pinion is now tight enough, the hour wheel is free on the pinion, there is just one more thing to check before we are ready to proceed with the dial and hands. That one thing is the condition of the teeth of all the wheels, including the intersetting wheels.

Illustration 99—Cutting tweezers.

Examine the teeth of the cannon pinion, minute wheel and hour wheel closely. Any worn or rough places, bent teeth, or other obstruction here will cause the watch to stop quickly. Examine the inter-setting wheels too. They should be equally free. There should be no oil under the inter-setting wheels at any time.

Practical Watch Hand Adjusting

When the dial is down and the dial screws are tight, the hour wheel pipe must be free in the dial. Now push on the hour hand and push it down until it is flush with the pipe of the hour wheel. Follow with the minute hand and push it down as far as it should go on the pinion. Now with the tweezer point test the hour wheel to see that it has enough tolerance to be free in both side shake and end shake.

Sometimes a snug fitting hour hand will cause the hour wheel to bind on the pinion barrel. When this happens, fit a larger hour hand, or ream out the present one, or ream out the hour wheel a little more. Perhaps this latter course is the safest and most satisfactory one. The hour wheel must be free — that is, must not bind in any position. (See illustrations 100 and 101)

To adjust the hands, press the hour hand down until it will carry completely around the dial just enough above the dial not to touch at any place, and to free the second hand. Then adjust the minute hand until it will just pass freely over the hour hand at any and all positions. Turn the watch dial down and see that the hands are still free. By pressing the hands as close to the dial as space will permit, we free them from the close fitting crystals of today.

Much hand trouble is caused by a too-low crystal. For that reason, it is best not to use the Mi-concave crystal at all. It is a good glass, but does not give the hands sufficient room. The Mi-Chevee glass gives the hands more room and also gives the watch a better appearance. (See illustration 102)

If a watch that otherwise seems perfect continues to run slow, or if the hands are inclined to hang occasionally, it is well to test the hands against the crystal.

In many cases you can look at the crystal with your eye glass and see where the minute hand has made a smooth mark all around the crystal. In a case of this kind, you know the hand is too high, or the glass is too low. One or both should be changed.

If you are not sure about the hand touching the glass, place just a small bit of oil on the highest part of the minute hand, then put the

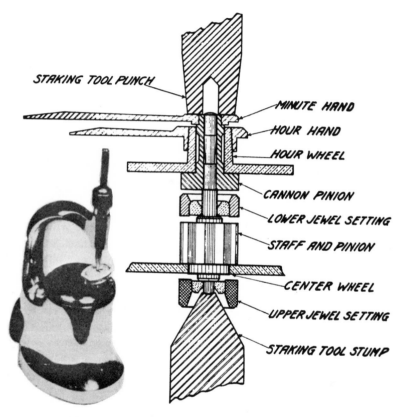

Illustrations 100, 101—Dialing and replacing hands. By using a staking tool to replace the hour and minute hands the center upper jewel is protected. The hands also become flush with the top of the hour wheel and cannon pinion, allowing a more perfect hour wheel freedom and more perfect hand clearance.

bevel in place and turn the hands around several times. If it touches the glass in any place, it will leave a smear of oil there.

One other problem is the military service watch and the nurse's watch with the sweep second hand. Instead of being placed on the extension of the 4th wheel pinion, the sweep second hand works on a very small pinion which comes through the center post. It is operated by a sixth wheel placed on an extension of the top pinion of the third wheel. This 6th wheel meshes with a small pinion extending through the center post. The seconds are marked off around the outside of the dial.

This assembly is not difficult to repair. But it does cause some trouble due to the fact it is somewhat higher than the minute hand and must be free from the minute hand and the crystal. The only trouble with the sweep second is removing the sixth wheel when taking the watch down. It is done by turning clockwise several rounds until it turns loose.

Split seconds, repeaters, chronometers and the like have multiple hands all of which require special attention. Better not tackle any of these until you have been repairing watches a long time. They require both skill and experience.

Cleaning Dials the Professional Way

For the watch repair job that comes into the store or the shop, there are certain rules that should be followed religiously. One of these is cleaning the case and dial.

For cleaning cases, a polishing machine is needed. All that is necessary is to follow instructions for polishing cases. However, for the beginner, there are two or three things to keep in mind. Do not attempt to polish a chain on a rotation buff. Better just wash the chains.

For the cases themselves, after they have been buffed properly, they should be boiled or heated rather hot in any good cleaning solution. "Sparkel," a powder especially put up for jewelry cleaning, is one of the best cleaners. If no good cleaner is available, ordinary laundry soap, household ammonia, warm water, and a good stiff wash brush will do an excellent job.

After the washing is completed, the case should be thoroughly dried. All steel parts, such as case springs, stems and sleeves, will rust unless all water is removed and they are heated until thoroughly dry.

This extra work adds sparkle to the finished job. The customer cannot see the work you have done inside. It can be appreciated only if it performs well after the watch is delivered to him. But if you have cleaned and polished his case, that will be evident immediately. It is not only part of the job you have contracted to do, it is that added touch thats ets your work apart from the other fellow's.

Everything said in the last paragraph pertaining to the cleaning of cases applies two-fold in the finishing and cleaning of dials. The old type hard enameled dial required little cleaning. But it is gradually passing out of the picture. Only a few pocket watches still use it.

With the more streamlined watches now in popular use, the metal dial with either raised numerals or black numerals are most in use. These dials require considerable care.

Perhaps the safest way to clean the average dial is to immerse it in a cyanide solution and then quickly neutralize the cyanide by im-

Illustration 102—Standard thickness watch crystals and how they are kept. Good crystals must preserve that thin streamline appearance of modern thin watches, yet allow plenty of space for hands and center post. They should be tough and springy, with perfectly ground edges; and perfectly sized. Fitting must be easy and economical.

mersing in running water and washing with simple baking soda. This may be done with an old tooth brush or any good scrub brush.

If the dial is sterling silver with baked enamel numerals, such as now used on most Hamilton bracelet watches, cleaning may be an even simpler job. First, to give the dial a new appearance, wash with baking soda. Then hold over a small alcohol flame until the dial gets very hot. When it reaches the correct temperature, it will gradually return to its original color. Remove from the flame at once and let cool.

Warning: this cannot be done with cheap dials such as are used on most watches. Heat will ruin them immediately. Better confine it to the Hamilton and certain other high grade watches. If you are not positive about the quality of the dial, better clean with soda and let it go at that.

Successful Friction Jewel Work

The past few years have witnessed some radical changes in the manufacture and repair of watches. Most of the changes in repairing have been brought about by the use of a few time saving machines.

For many years the watchmaking industry was inclined to remain more or less stable. That was due, more or less, to the reluctance of the watchmaker to accept anything that is new or different.

A good illustration of this is a story that went the rounds many years back. It is worth telling for the lesson it teaches.

A traveling man was making his first trip through the mountains of Kentucky. By the wayside he found a farmer carrying pumpkins up the hill in a sack. He had a rock in one end of the sack. He put a pumpkin in the other end, threw it over his shoulder, and carried it up the hill to the house.

After he had removed the pumpkin, he carried the rock back to the field for another pumpkin. The traveling man stopped and watched for a while and stepped forward with a suggestion.

"Why don't you", he asked, "take two pumpkins over your shoulder in the same way? Then you will not have to bring the rock back each time."

The farmer spit tobacco juice across three pumpkin rows, striking a bug squarely between the eyes. Then he spoke.

"My Grandpappy carried this rock with pumpkins. My Pappy carried it up the hill with pumpkins. If it was good enough for them, hits good enough for me."

That, I am sorry to say, was somewhat the attitude taken by most watchmakers to anything new or different. After World War I, however, manufacturers began building wrist watches for their own survival. Incidentally, it saved the jewelry industry from oblivion. Gradually the tool manufacturers began bringing out new and improved

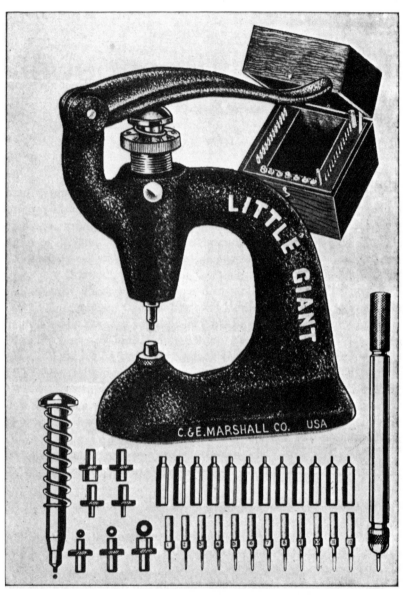

Illustration 103—Friction jeweling outfit. *Friction Jeweling means the setting of watch jewels that are held in place by friction, instead of being burnished into the plate or setting. Friction Jewels are now being used in new model watches by all of the leading manufacturers, both American and Swiss. They are of greatest value, however, to the repairman, who can use them to replace old-type burnished-in jewels. With the proper equipment, the new Friction Jewels can be*

tools and by high pressure selling began placing them with the younger, more liberal minded workmen. Today they are universally
accepted.

One of these tools is the Friction Jeweling Outfit. (See illustration
103) Another is the cleaning machine, and later the Watchmaster Rate
Recorder. The last two to be discussed later.

Up until a few years back, all Swiss type jewels were set in bezels.
American watches used a slightly different jewel, as seen in your 16s
Hamilton. Here the jewels are set in bezels but the bezels are made
into jewel settings, so the entire setting may be replaced in case of
breakage or other damage.

In the Swiss watch, however, the setting was part of the plate.
The bezel was made in the plate and the jewel had to be fitted into
the bezel, and then the bezel was burnished over it to hold it secure.
This was a very satisfactory arrangement, but required a lot of time
and skill to do correctly and neatly. Furthermore, after a watch had
had several jewels replaced, the setting usually became damaged to
such an extent that no one, however skilled, could do a fine job of repairing, without cutting a new setting.

Some years back the friction jewel was developed. In the middle
thirties the C. & E. Marshall Company introduced the first friction jeweling outfit in America.

The jewel itself differs from the former type. The friction jewel has
straight edges the same thickness as the center of the jewel. Instead
of resting in a bezel which must be opened and closed, it is simply
pushed friction tight into a hole reamed with a special tool.

To fit a jewel quickly, you first push out the old jewel. Use a
reamer to guage the size of the hole. If the diameter does not cor-
respond with your jewel, you may select the next larger reamer and
enlarge the hole to the correct size. The number 9 reamer is the same
size as the jewel that is listed on the chart as diameter 90. Number
10 is 100, and so on.

---

set in one-tenth the time required for setting burnished-in jewels, and the job is
not only more secure, but more accurate and more satisfactory in every way.
The principle of Friction Jeweling is very simple. After the old jewel has been
removed the hole in the plate setting is reamed out perfectly straight by a pre-
cision-gauged self centering straight-hole reamer. The Friction Jewel, which is
more rugged than the old type, being much thicker throughout the entire diameter,
is pressed into the hole either flush or to any desired depth in the plate or setting.

Select the correct pivot size and the correct diameter, then merely place the jewel over the hole and use the pusher to push it into position. You will find it sufficiently tight. If it must be raised or lowered, this can be done by pushing further in, or reversing the plate and pushing it back until the desired position is reached.

This jeweling tool also has another time-saving use. Often old watches have worn pivot holes. Perhaps they have been closed so many times the plate is too thin to do a good closing job. If so, select a plate jewel from the outfit, get the correct pivot and diameter size and set it in the plate. You will find that it can be done within five minutes at a very low cost, and you have another hole that will never again have to be closed.

Since almost all new watches have the friction type jewel today, the friction jeweling tool is indispensable to the modern workman.

Using the Watch Cleaning Machine

In the first lessons of this course we discussed the cleaning of a watch in some detail. At that time the cleaning machine was not discussed because the beginner would not care to invest so much money at the start.

For the man who expects to follow watchmaking as a profession, however, the cleaning machine is another of the once rejected tools that he will not want to be without. It is a simple machine and does the work so easily and so well that it is hard to realize that just a few years back good workmen would not even look at one, much less use one.

I stress the watchmaker's reluctance to use anything new for a reason. I want you to know something about the history of watchmaking in recent years, and I want you to make up your mind now NOT to become set in your ways. Never reject anything because it is new. If it is new, try it out, give it every chance to help you. That way leads to progress.

The present day machine is somewhat different from the original. Also its use is somewhat different from that originally suggested. When the first machines appeared, their maker advocated removing only the dial and hands, balance assembly, and mainspring. The idea was to save the time required to take down and assemble the rest of the watch.

Experienced workmen know the dangers involved in a job of this kind and would have none of it. So for long years they refused to see anything good in a cleaning machine.

But there is always someone who will experiment, however, and to the experimenter the world owes a debt of gratitude. No less so with the cleaning machine. (See illustrations 104 and 105)

To use for best results, take the watch down in the usual manner and place the parts in the basket. You will find there a place for the large plates, a smaller place for the smaller plates, and still smaller compartments for cap jewels, screws, and other small parts. (Do not run the balance through the cleaning solution.) Any good cleaning solution may be used. Let the watch stay in the cleaner for a few minutes. If it is very badly spotted or corroded, let it stay longer. Then bring it up above the solution which should reach approximately half way up the jar. Spin the basket fast enough to sling off the surplus solution. Then dip it into the next jar with clear water. This will remove the rest of the solution on the watch.

Then the last two jars should be half filled with a good rinsing solution. Spin the watch in each of these for a few seconds or longer,

Illustration 104—Watch cleaning machine. Does a complete and thorough cleaning job in 3 minutes. Machines are approved and recommended by many leading horologists as the best way of cleaning a watch. Leaves no sawdust, cyanide, pegwood or chalk. No loss of parts while brushing and no trouble due to dirty brushes.

then swing around into the dryer. Let it dry thoroughly before assembling.

If your solutions are good, you will find it has done a much better job of cleaning than you can do by hand, and it has been less than half the time and trouble.

Remember, the last rinsing solution should always be clear and clean. When it becomes clouded, it does not dry the watch properly and should be replaced.

Another important thing is to remember that the cleaning solution will cause rust if it is not all removed from the steel parts. That is why rinsing is so important. The rinsing solution will quickly evaporate

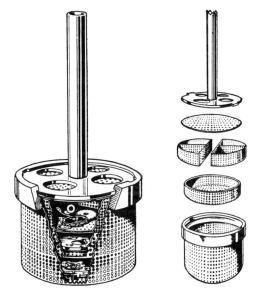

Illustration 105 — Container used in watch cleaning machine. Perforated monel metal.

of its own accord. However, it is better to have the heater hot when the basket goes in it so it will dry the watch very quickly. This keeps the plates from becoming spotted and also speeds up the work.

For your own protection as well as that of your customer, do not try to clean a watch without taking it down. Use all short cuts possible but this will prove not to be a short cut in the long run.

The Peerless Cleaning Machine has several distinct advantages. Not the least of these is the switch which permits the basket to oscillate in the solution. This assures your watch a thorough cleaning as all parts are bound to be in contact with the solution during this rapid swishing back and forth.

Also the automatic cut off on the dryer prevents the watch getting too hot. In buying a machine for your own use some day, study these points and consider their merits.

8-Day Clock---Care and Repair

For the man who proposes to become a professional watchmaker, the eight day clock is something to be avoided like the plague. You cannot do good watch work if you switch back and forth from clock work to watch work all during the day. So, if you expect to be a good watchmaker and follow that career, then you may well pass up these lessons on the eight day clock.

If, on the other hand, you expect to operate your own repair shop or do odd jobs in your spare time, then it is well to know how to repair the old family standby. No one else wants to associate with it. Therefore, perhaps you may well make a good living doing nothing else. Many men do.

In principal, the clock differs little from the watch. In application, it is entirely different.

For the purpose of this lesson, get any fairly good inexpensive eight day clock. First, we remove the hands and dial. Of course, the pendulum must come off, too. Then you will find there are four wood screws holding the movement into the case. Remove these screws with a medium size clock screwdriver.

Observe that the clock has two trains. One side is the running side. The other is the striking side. They each are somewhat like the watch train in that they start with a mainspring and graduate down to the verge wheel and fly wheel respectively.

First, let us discuss the running side. The verge wheel is somewhat like the escape wheel of the watch. The verge of the clock is very much like the pallet fork of the watch. The verge, however, has a verge wire extending down from it. On this wire is a loop end. Through this end goes the pendulum rod. The pendulum rod operates from a stationary post attached to the front plate. It extends downward with a hook on the end to hold the pendulum ball.

Note all these features carefully, because they are of utmost importance in repairing and making a clock keep time.

If the clock is expensive enough and the repair price charged is enough to justify the work, it is well to take the clock down and clean it piece by piece just as we did with the watch. This can be done with the more expensive, better made models. With the ordinary eight day clock, however, neither the value of the clock nor the repair charge justifies the time necessary to do this. Therefore, we must find a satisfactory short cut.

If an ordinary cleaning job is all that is needed, it is well to fill a small glass bowl with the same cleaning solution used to clean watches. See that the bowl is deep enough to cover the clock completely with solution. Before putting the clock in the solution, it is well to place clamps over the springs. (See illustration 106) These clamps prevent the springs from unwinding and causing plenty trouble. When the clamp is around the spring, use a heavy bench clock key to hold the winding arbor while you release the click. Let the spring down slowly until it is safely into the clamp. Then you will notice there is no power on the train.

Illustration 106—Mainspring for American 8-day clock; in clasp.

Now remove the verge from the clock, permitting the train wheels to operate freely in the solution. Now immerse the movement completely and let it remain in the solution for several minutes. Then with a small, stiff brush, go over the movement from end to end. Brush the pinions and around the pivots and pivot holes. See that all caked oil and other foreign matter is removed. When the clock is thoroughly cleaned, it should be rinsed in the same manner as the watch, and dried. The verge, too, should be cleaned and examined to see that the ends are not worn.

Skilful Clock Repairing

Repairing a worn verge is one of the jobs that requires some skill. Many times we find that some foreign abrasive has got onto the verge wheel teeth. Being brass, they are soft and when thoroughly charged with the abrasive they become veritable laps grinding away on the ends of the steel verge. This accounts for the harder steel points being worn without any sign of wear on the softer brass parts. It also indicates that the clock has been running for a long time without oil.

Of course the best way to repair a worn verge is to replace it with a new one. That is also the quickest way. Use the old verge wire as a sample and bend the new verge wire in the same manner and the same length. Then place the verge on the clock. If it was made by the manufacturer for that clock, it should work with little adjustment.

If, on the other hand, there is no verge available — which is often the case — then we must contrive to do a good repair job on the old one. It can be done, provided it is not too badly worn.

To do it we need a good fast cutting oilstone well charged with oil. Note the angle of the impulse face of the verge. It must not be altered, this angle. Therefore, we must cut down the verge with a flat, straight motion on the oil stone. Hold it firmly at the right angle and pull it back firmly and flat against the stone, stroke upon stroke. When the worn slot disappears, switch to a fine cut very hard stone for polishing the end. Be sure you have not changed the angle. Now polish the face until it is bright and smooth. Turn the verge around and do the same with the other end. Do not overlook the difference in the angle of the impulse faces.

When the faces are finished they will be somewhat shorter than originally. How much shorter depends on how much had to be removed because of the wear. This difference calls for another adjustment to offset it. Just as in a watch, every action brings about a reaction. One change must be made to compensate for another.

Before proceeding with adjusting the verge, however, let's take up the clock movement where we left it. It is now dry and ready to oil. Using a good grade clock oil, we carefully place a very small drop of oil on or around each pivot of the train. Also a bit on the click. The spring itself gets a more generous supply. This being the motor power of the clock, it must be kept operating smoothly. The coils of the spring should be released, dried, and oiled well.

Oil the verge pinion, and place it in position. You will find the verge is held in position with a post which is tight on the movement, but can be moved upward or downward. There is also a small drop of oil placed on each end of the verge. Now wind the running side a few rounds.

By moving the verge back and forth, you will notice the long sweep it makes. Perhaps two or more teeth will escape with each stroke; this particularly if the verge had to be faced down somewhat. However, to correct it, force upward the arm holding the verge pivot. It will swing up until the verge escapes just as it should. A little experimenting will be necessary to get the desired result. Should you over-do it, push it back downward again.

LESSON FIFTY-THREE

Profitable Verge Work

Now place the pendulum spring or pendulum rod into position. Wind the spring almost all the way up and remove the clamp from the spring. Now place the movement into the clock and replace the screws holding it firmly in place.

Set the clock up now on a level table or work bench, and hang the pendulum ball on the rod. We are now ready to put the clock in beat. The beat of the clock is more important to its running or timekeeping than is the beat of the watch. The average clock will not run long if it is very much out of beat.

Before attempting to put it in beat, however, we must have certain things correct. One of these is the loop on the verge wire through which the pendulum rod vibrates. This loop must be open just enough to permit the rod to vibrate freely. But it must not be open any more than is needed for free action. Just for experience, open the loop somewhat and set the clock to running. Notice what a short, jerky motion it makes. Also note it will not keep time. (See illustration 107)

Now close the loop over the pendulum spring until there is just enough tolerance to permit free action. If either the rod or the loop seem to be rough at this juncture, place just a tiny drop of light weight watch oil on them here. This often removes the friction and brings about a better motion.

Now we are ready for the beat itself. No doubt you have heard many times that a clock must be level to run. In a sense this is true. But actually it is not necessarily true. It must be in beat. To be level does not necessarily mean to be in beat. Again the sound must be your guide. It is well to have the clock on a level place. By rights, it should be put in beat in the exact position in which it is expected to run. Since this cannot always be done, better get it perfectly level and in beat; then it will remain that way anywhere, if the same conditions prevail.

Some people make a mark in the center of the bottom of the clock, and attempt to get the pendulum to hang directly over the mark. This is of questionable value. Remember this: a clock can be put in beat and made to keep time with one end an inch higher than the other. This is seldom necessary. But it proves that the level idea is good, but not essential.

Again the tick and the tock must be of equal duration. Let the pendulum swing to rest where it will, and notice which end of the

Illustration 107—Clock verge. In ordering verges from a supply house send sample, if possible, to insure correct handling.

verge is resting against the verge wheel tooth. Now swing the pendulum to the other side of the clock just enough to get the tooth to escape. Let the pendulum come back to rest, and see if the lock is approximately the same on each side of the verge. It should be exactly the same.

The lock is changed by bending the verge wire between the verge itself, and the loop going over the pendulum wire. To do a perfect job this wire should remain straight, and the bending should be down within one half inch of the verge. This, however, is not easy to do and only a slight adjustment will not make any difference. Notice how changing the wire will change the positions of the verge itself; thus changing the lock of the escapement. When the lock looks even to the eye, start the pendulum to swinging and after the extra power of your motion has died down, and it is swinging on its own power, we will make another test.

Listen closely to the tick and tock. If they appear even to the ear, they are probably close. So to hear better, place the point of your clock screwdriver against the clock and place the handle firmly against the ear. This conveys the sound directly to the ear drum and makes an excellent listening device. With it you can detect any variation that was not heard before. Adjust the verge until the stroke is even, steady, and of the same duration. Let it run for some time and test it again. Sometimes they settle down and have to have a second adjusting.

If it checks right on the second go-round, you are ready to replace the dial and hands.

Replacing Clock Mainspring

In the better mantle clocks built in recent years it not difficult to replace springs. They have barrels somewhat like watches. Less expensive models have plates in sections, making it easy to remove the plate directly over the mainspring, and slip it out.

First, however, we place a clamp over the spring, if possible to do so, so it may be removed without damage to the clock or your hands. If it is broken and cannot be clamped, we must be careful to remove the plate directly over it, and work it out without letting it get away from you. The new springs come according to measurements in inches of width and length. If you are not sure about having the genuine spring for that clock, replace it with one the same width and length, and you will probably be right.

Springs have clamps around them when bought. All you need do is place it over the arbor on the main wheel, and see that it catches. Oil it carefully and place it into the clock. Be sure the plate screws are tight before winding up fully.

If by chance it is an older clock that does not have sectional plates, then the entire top plate must come off before the old spring can be removed or a new one inserted. To do this, we clamp both springs and let the power off them. This is a dengerous operation so watch yourself and protect your hands and fingers.

When the train wheels are free on either side, remove the plate screws and move the plate up just enough to remove the wheel with the broken spring. Be careful, meantime, not to move the other wheels of the train; for on the striking side particularly the wheels must be in a certain position, place the plate over the train and see that all pivots are in their pivot holes just as in the train of a watch. In the clock there are many more pivots to look after. Therefore, it is somewhat more difficult to do.

Adjusting and Regulating

The striking side of an eight day clock is usually on the right side of the movement as you face the clock. The train is very much like the running side with several notable differences. First, the fly wheel acts as a governor, holding the striking down to a normal speed. Should the governor slip on the pivot, as it sometimes does, the strikes are so fast that they are run together as one sound. Therefore, the spring holding this fly wheel or governor in position should be tight enough to prevent slipping at all times.

Perhaps the best way to understand the working of the striking train is to observe it closely. Make the movement strike over and over while watching a different part each time. Learn just what each part does and how it does it. Each wheel plays a part. It would take several lessons to try to explain each action to you. Still, perhaps you would be more confused than you now are. So let us say, then, the best way is to teach yourself the proper function of each part. Notice then how each one performs along strictly mechanical lines. It does what it does simply because it must do it. There is nothing mysterious about it.

To learn to adjust any trouble we must first learn how it should be when correct. Then we can quickly tell if it is not as it should be. Make whatever change is necessary. This is time-consuming, but the best way in the end. It is not complicated but simply something you don't learn well until you do it. You cannot gain too much experience.

Now to regulate the clock. Many modern clocks have a small end on the back of the key. This end fits into the small keyhole at the very top of the dial. One side is marked slow; the other fast. Insert this key, turn it, and watch the action on the other side. To make the clock run faster, the pendulum is moved upward. To make it run slower, the pendulum is moved downward, or extended.

This is easy to understand. To extend the length of the pendulum spring naturally lengthens the stoke. Thus it takes the pendulum longer to complete its arc. Conversely, to shorten the length of the pendulum rod naturally makes the strokes of shorter duration, causing the clock to run faster.

This method of regulating mentioned above is good for a small variation, such as is needed when a clock has been cleaned or is in need of cleaning. However, in replacing a broken pendulum spring, or on the larger clock a pendulum rod, be sure the new one is the same length as the old one. To make it shorter or longer requires further regulation.

Another method is with a thumb screw on the pendulum rod just

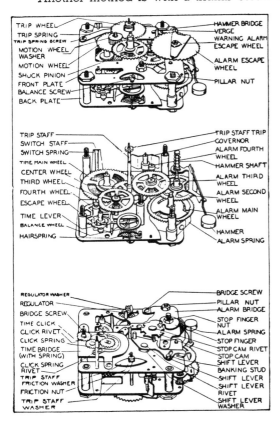

TRIP WHEEL
TRIP SPRING
TRIP SPRING SCREW
MOTION WHEEL WASHER
MOTION WHEEL
SHUCK PINION
FRONT PLATE
BALANCE SCREW
BACK PLATE

HAMMER BRIDGE
VERGE
WARNING ALARM
ESCAPE WHEEL
ALARM ESCAPE WHEEL
PILLAR NUT

TRIP STAFF
SWITCH STAFF
SWITCH SPRING
TIME MAIN WHEEL
CENTER WHEEL
THIRD WHEEL
FOURTH WHEEL
ESCAPE WHEEL
TIME LEVER
BALANCE WHEEL
HAIRSPRING

TRIP STAFF TRIP
GOVERNOR
ALARM FOURTH WHEEL
HAMMER SHAFT
ALARM THIRD WHEEL
ALARM SECOND WHEEL
ALARM MAIN WHEEL
HAMMER
ALARM SPRING

Illustration 108—This is an illustration of the present Westclox Big Ben chime alarm with quiet tick and 2-voiced alarm. Many of these parts fit the original chime alarm model (Big Ben) that had a flat glass.

REGULATOR WASHER
REGULATOR
BRIDGE SCREW
TIME CLICK
CLICK RIVET
CLICK SPRING
TIME BRIDGE (WITH SPRING)
CLICK SPRING RIVET
TRIP STAFF FRICTION WASHER
FRICTION NUT
TRIP STAFF WASHER

BRIDGE SCREW
PILLAR NUT
ALARM BRIDGE
STOP FINGER NUT
ALARM SPRING
STOP FINGER
STOP CAM RIVET
STOP CAM
SHIFT LEVER
BANKING STUD
SHIFT LEVER
SHIFT LEVER RIVET
SHIFT LEVER WASHER

below the pendulum ball. To shift the screw upward raises the ball, and thus the center of gravity upward, causing the watch to gain. Letting the screw down also drops the pendulum ball, thus lowering the center of gravity and causing the clock to make a longer stroke.

Should you get tied up on a difficult job where the entire length of the pendulum rod will not make the clock run slow enough, there is still another method. This is the addition of weight to the pendulum ball. Many times a spot of soft solder on the back of the ball will give the necessary weight. If the rod is somewhat too short and no other is available, a small amount of lead added in the center of the pendulum ball so as not to change the center of gravity, will often give the necessary weight.

Let me stress, however, that these last two similar suggestions are offered only as a last resort. They may have to be used on some obsolete models. On most modern models, whatever material needed for ordinary repairs can be had from the better supply houses.

Should you go into clock repairing, you will find that most eight day clocks have different construction in one way or another. Seldom will you find two with the same striking assembly. Even the pendulum springs are different, of different length and weight. Here again the best suggestion is to use your good judgement. Get the fundamentals; then use your head and you will have little trouble.

Not only do clocks differ in construction, but some are far more sensitive than others to regulate. This is hard to explain. Perhaps a half turn on a regulator screw will effect one twice as much as another. This makes all regulation largely a matter of guess work, or trial and error. As soon as you discover how sensitive the regulator is, then you will have little difficulty finding the correct spot to get the desired result.

Making Money on Alarm Clock Work

The alarm clock is of simple construction. Perhaps the most complicated thing about most of them is getting the movement out of the case. The only conclusion is that some manufacturers must have hired mystery story writers to design the case construction of their clocks.

Before discussing the clock further, let it be said that neither the writer nor the publisher wishes to be partial to or against any clock or make of clocks. However, if you confine your study and actual repairs to the models of one manufacturer alone, you will be making a wise move. The Big Ben and Baby Ben and allied models are well constructed, easily repaired clocks. So take a hint, and confine yourself to these alone. (See illustrations 108 to 114)

Actual repairing of the alarm clock is something of a cross between the eight day clock and the watch. Here, once again, the value of the clock and the maximum prices that can be charged for repairs, will hardly justify taking the clock down to repair as we do the watch. Therefore, we first take it out of the case and remove the dial and hands. When this is done, you will find that by unpinning the hairspring and releasing the two screws which act as balance jewels, the balance will lift right out of the movement.

Clean the balance well, seeing that all grease, oil, and other foreign matter is removed from the staff and hairspring. Now chuck it up in your lathe and see that the pivots are running true. Then use a very sharp graver or a fast cutting oil stone, and hone the pivots down to a long very keen needle-like point. This pivot should slope back very gradually and retain its symmetery all the way. When the keen point is reached, polish the pivot smooth and bright, just as you would polish a watch pivot. Do this to both ends.

Now immerse the entire movement into the cleaning solution and clean just as you did the eight day clock. Using a small, stiff brush,

see that all pinions are thoroughly cleaned. Pay particular attention
to the pivots and pivot holes of the train. They must be clean and
free. Also they must be completely dried by using a clean rinse and
heating.

Once again all pivots and other parts where there is friction,
whether turning or not, should be oiled with either a light grade clock
oil or a good grade watch oil. The alarm clock requires more oil than
the watch, but not so much as the eight day clock. The springs must
be thoroughly cleaned and well oiled. So must the escape wheel and
fork receive special care.

We are now ready to assemble the clock. This is the only difficult thing about repairing the clock. Here precision is as necessary
as in the watch. Here, too, your watch training will be of great aid.

The balance screws into which worked the balance pivots may be
replaced if they are worn. If no new ones are available, then it is

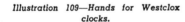

Illustration 109—Hands for Westclox   *Illustrations 110, 111—Hand setters.*
clocks.

well to polish the bearings by chucking them in the lathe, spinning
them true, and using a good grade diamantine on the point of a piece
of hard peg wood. Repeat this operation by spinning the bearing at
various speeds until it, too, has a bright smooth surface. Then clean
thoroughly and insert in the movement just as it was before being
removed.

Leaving the bearings open enough to permit the balance to go in,
we insert the balance and then tighten the bearings just enough to
prohibit its falling out. We now have the balance turning freely in its
assembly. It now must be brought around against the pallet fork in an
overbanked position, then bring the end of the hairspring through the
regulator pins and into the stud. Pin the hairspring as nearly in the
original position as possible.

After it is pinned in such manner that the roller pin faces squarely
into the pallet fork while the fork is squarely along the line of centers

—that is, resting exactly half way between the banking pins, it should be in beat. This cannot be determined, however, until the spring is flat, and true in the round. The regulator should be placed in the center of the index, and the watch regulated by changing the pinning of the spring in the stud. This is a difficult adjustment, but is made necessary by the fact the alarm clock does not have a removable hairspring stud. By experimenting a little, however, you will become very proficient in the proper pinning of the hairspring.

Should it run fast, pin the spring a little longer. Should it run slow, pin the spring a little shorter. Each time this requires the adjust-

Illustration 112—Big Ben time spring with barrel. New chime model.

Illustration 113—Big Ben time spring with barrel. Old chime model.

ing of the spring in the flat and in the round. Also it requires the moving of the spring collet in order to bring the roller pin to the proper position to put the clock in beat. Putting the alarm clock in beat is accomplished exactly as putting a watch in beat. Bear in mind, also, that though a clock may run if not properly in beat, it is not likely to keep accurate time. Furthermore, you have no assurance that it will continue to run. It is much less trouble to put it in beat while you are working with it than it is later after it has been put in the case. So do the job right while you are doing it and it will save much time.

Since the alarm clock sets in an upright position at all times, it is necessary to adjust it to only one position.

Alarm Clock Repair Methods

The better alarm clocks are so constructed that the replacing of springs is not a difficult job. When the movement is out of the case, you will notice that there is a small plate holding each spring in position. To remove the spring it is necessary to remove only the plate holding it. New springs are available from any good jeweler's supply house. It is hardly ever advisable to attempt to repair a broken spring. The genuine spring is so easily inserted and fits into the clock without any fitting to be done. The strength and length are correct. There-

Illustration 114—Alarm spring for Big Ben chime alarm clock, all models.

fore, all that is needed is a little oil placed on the spring and then wound up. The springs are fitted into a barrel. Therefore, no clamps are needed or used. (See illustration 115)

In the case of the mainspring, you will find the ratchet is also on the barrel. So in case of a broken ratchet or any other trouble with the ratchet or ratchet spring, it is well to remove the barrel completely and replace it with a new one. This is a less expensive method than trying to repair the faulty material.

After the hands and dial have been removed, the hour and minute hands go back just as those of a watch. They are adjusted in the same manner. However, the fitting of the alarm hand is somewhat more complicated.

In order to understand the alarm thoroughly, study its action while the movement is out of the case. Turn the alarm hand until it "goes off"; that is to say, until the clock alarms. Notice what action takes place making the clock alarm. Place oil on all friction parts of the alarm.

Now in placing the alarm hand back in its proper position, first set the hour and minute hands to a given hour. Then turn the alarm hand key until the alarm goes off. Then place the alarm hand on its pivot pointing to the exact hour to which the hour and minute hands are set. For example, if the hour and minute hands are set at 9 o'clock, the alarm key is turned until the clock alarms. Thus we know it has alarmed at nine o'clock. Hence we set the alarm hand at 9 o'clock. Now in order to test this, turn the alarm hand to another hour, and proceed to turn the hour and minute hands clockwise until that given hour is reached. The clock should alarm at that time, provided it is set to alarm. If it does not, then it must be adjusted until it does.

Establishing a Modern Repair System

When you have successfully completed the lessons up to this point, you will be well on the road toward becoming a good watchmaker. You will be able to do simple repairs on plain watches and clocks. What you need now is experience and still more experience.

Keep this volume handy and at any time you do not thoroughly understand how any particular job should be handled, consult these lessons. But use it only for consultation. You must know the work so well that the use of the book will be unnecessary, except for unusual jobs.

If you expect to make watchmaking a career; then my advice to you is try to get employment somewhere with a more experienced watchmaker who will help with suggestions as you encounter difficult jobs. Some watchmakers will help in every way possible. Some will not. The latter kind usually resent being asked to reveal any of their precious knowledge. There is little you can do with this type of fellow but ignore him. Do that in big doses. You do have one consolation — he is usually the type who knows very little and is afraid to tell anything for fear he will reveal his ignorance.

There are many books dealing with some phase of watchmaking. If you feel the need of such books, by all means get them. Study them diligently. You can learn much by studying as you work. However, the most important single thing is to be willing and anxious to learn; do not hesitate to ask questions of anyone who will give you intelligent answers. Remember what you read and are told. Apply it when the occasion arises. That way you will become a good workman.

Should you decide to operate your own repair shop, the field today is almost unlimited. There is a need for good workmen almost everywhere. But in operating your own repair shop, you must do two things:

(a) You must give quick service.

(b) It must be good.

In establishing you own shop, one of the essential things, whether you are in some place by yourself or in some store with arrangement to operate the shop — is to have a system for everything.

A system for handling the work.

A system for handling the customer.

A system for keeping your tools.

And perhaps most important of all, a system for keeping your material. (See illustration 116)

In some so-called modern shops you will find little system for keeping material. This is a serious indictment of the shop, as it retards production.

In a busy shop, the watchmaker should not have to spend an average of 1% of his time looking for material. Yet in some shops crowns are all dumped into a large box. When a crown is needed the

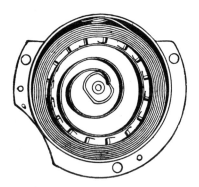

Illustration 115—Westclox mainspring. Big Ben leg model and base model (except chime alarm).

watchmaker scratches around through the lot until he decides he does not have what he needs. Then he orders a dozen crowns, uses the one he wants and dumps the rest in with the lot he already has so he cannot find them when he wants them.

This sort of thing is still being done by watchmakers who are supposed to be up-to-date. Good workmen spend thirty minutes fitting a piece of material that should be found and fitted in three minutes, and could have been with a well kept system. Furthermore, a system keeps you from overbuying, thus actually saving you money. The little time required to keep it straight is repaid many times over in the time it saves. This is particularly true of the frequently used items such as staffs, jewels, stems, crowns, mainsprings, etc.

Another consideration is space. If you have a small shop or must confine your shop to a small space in a store, it is well to consider a complete Add-A-Unit system. It confines the maximum amount of material into the minimum space allowable and offers efficient time saving charts.

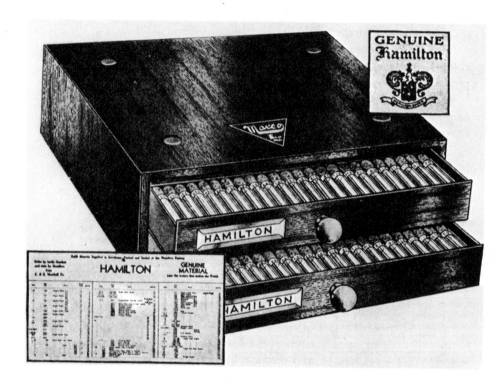

Illustration 116—System of genuine watch factory material. Elgin, Waltham, Hamilton, Illinois and other watch companies each have on the market a cabinet of watch parts comprising all the most needed parts for their respective watches. The material in these cabinets is placed in small numbered bottles with a corresponding descriptive chart to make it easy to select any part for that particular make of watch. This illustration shows Hamilton parts in a standardized cabinet put out by a supply house.

American watch manufacturers put up a more or less complete system for keeping their own material. But they build these without thought to appearance of your shop or the space you may have available. They leave a few empty bottles to permit expansion, but they seldom get around to supplying you with the new charts to cover the new numbers they bring out from time to time. For that reason, you seldom find two systems that are the same. Each workman has arranged his material to suit himself. The cabinets supplied by one manufacturer will not fit over or under those made by another.

To overcome these handicaps and to conserve all possible time and space the C. & E. Marshall Company has designed a system of cabinets that cover all your needs in the least possible space. All the cabinets are of one size. They are of metal construction, stack perfectly, and are uniform in color.

Genuine material is worked into these cabinets just as the factory puts it up. Only genuine parts are furnished. Charts show the location of every item.

Mainsprings are listed according to number. First you determine the size of the spring by measuring it with the millimeter guage. On the chart you find the corresponding number for that particular size and length. Then you have only to open the cabinet and pick up the number indicated.

This system properly kept enables you to find and fit the correct mainspring in less than ten minutes. If you have no system, you will spend more time hunting for the correct spring, and then probably not find it. The above is true of all other items.

Another thing is the advantage of having everything convenient. With the properly arranged shop, any tool or piece of material can be reached without getting out of your chair. This is a distinct advantage when doing delicate work. When the more delicate jobs are to be done, it is better to arrange to do them when you are not likely to be disturbed. If you are forced to lay a job down at a critical point, when you get back you have forgotten where you were. So you start all over again. Meantime your nerves are no longer atuned to that particular job and you will probably find it more difficult to do than it would have been had you been permitted to continue with it originally. Therefore, try to keep the shop quiet as possible, and keep it away from the public if you can.

★　★　★　★　★

The buying of material is quite simple, provided you follow a few simple rules. When you are using the genuine material systems, all that is necessary is to specify whatever quantity desired, giving the cabinet bottle number and the name of the manufacturer. For example: material comes put up in 1/4 dozen lots. All you need do is write, "Please send 1/4 dozen Hamilton refill No. 30."

This will give you the item always found in bottle number 30.

In the American systems you will find two or three bottles carrying material such as staffs and jewels for the same watch. These items are the same except for different pivot sizes.

In Hamilton material you will find the tolerances somewhat closer than in other cabinets. For example, if the pivot is size 10, the jewel hole for that pivot will be size 10½. This gives you a tolerance of 1/200mm.

If you buy these items in correct pivot and hole sizes, keep them in their correct bottles in the cabinet, there is no guaging to be done. You will always have the exact size you want when you want it. If you fail to do this, then you must use a jewel hole guage to determine the correct hole size. (See illustration 117 and 118)

The above suggestions are not only time savers, but if you expect to do close timing, jewel hole tolerances must not be more than one full size. In wrist and other small watches, tolerances should be even closer.

It is almost impossible to over-stress the great importance of having and being able to get at the correct material at all times. Without material reasonably correct, you cannot hope to do the kind of work you must do.

In ordering material you must use a certain amount of judgment both as to quantity and to make. For example, supply houses often get letters containing an Elgin staff and stating "please send me one-fourth dozen WALTHAM staffs to sample." Then your supply house is on the spot. They want to serve you accurately and quickly. But in a case of this kind they do not know what you really want. Perhaps you want a Waltham staff and picked up the wrong sample. Maybe you want an Elgin staff like sample and merely wrote the word "Waltham" in an absent-minded moment. Either way they guess is likely to be wrong.

If they send you a staff for an Elgin like the sample, and you really wanted a Waltham, then you are disappointed and blame the supply house for not filling your order correctly.

Conversely, if they send what you ask for and you really wanted one like sample, regardless of make, again you and your customer are disappointed. If they hold the matter up until they can write you about it, perhaps you will have forgotten what you sent and may not have a copy of the order, so the matter becomes more and more befogged.

These things are stressed because, being new at the business, you are going to make some boners. We all do. But strive to know exactly what you want and state that fact briefly. Remember, the man

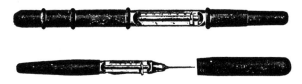

Illustrations 117, 118—Jewel Hole Gauge. A gauge necessary to most watchmakers. By simply slipping the fine needle point into the hole of the jewel, indicator will register the hole size on the index. Measures all sizes from .06 to .40 m/m. All metal with steel point and metal cap to protect point.

or woman filling that order wants to serve you — that is his living — but he knows only what you tell him. He knows material. If you want a certain piece and send a sample, he knows what it is the instant he sees it, no matter by what name you may call it. Save yourself much time and trouble by keeping your material straight, up to date, and in its place. Know what each piece is. Know which make of watch it is for. Study the different watches and their differences in construction. It is good information to have. Get it.

Crystals--- A Very Profitable Line

Crystals are not only a very profitable line, but a very essential one. Even if you did not fit crystals for your customers, you would need them for your own use. Many times you have to change an improperly fitted glass. Often they are too low, or not tight enough.

There are several types of glass. I am speaking first of the round crystal. First there is the Mi-Concave. This is a very heavy glass, but not a very satisfactory one. Its use is not recommended. True, it costs a few cents less than the better glass, but the other is more than worth the slight difference.

Then there is the Lentile glass. (These names designate the shape of the crystal). The lentile is a higher glass, giving the hands more working room, but it is somewhat streamlined and gives the watch a

Illustration 119—Crystal numbering system. How to select the right watch crystal immediately.

streamlined appearance. It is used largely on thin model watches. It is a very good crystal. But it has one fault. Its edges are not strong and chip rather easily.

Then there is, perhaps, the most generally satisfactory crystal of all — the Mi-Chevee. (See illustration 119) It has edges like the Mi-Concave, yet it is high like the Lentile, and really gives the hands more room than either of the other two.

Round crystals are numbered in 16ths. These numbers have no connection with the size of the watch. It is a numbering system used exclusively with and for crystals. For example, the label on the crystal will be printed to read 18-0/16. The next size will be 18-1/16, 18-2/16, 18-3/16, and so on to 18-15/16. The next size will be 19-0/16.

Today there are a limited number of pocket watches in use. Therefore, all sizes will not be used. However, it is well to have some of each size in the cabinet so you can take care of any emergency. Your crystal cabinet has numbered slots into which the crystals bearing that number should always be placed. This enables you to find the size you want.

How to Fit Fancy Crystals

You have observed that the round crystal is snapped into the bezel. This means that the glass is actually forced through a space smaller than the glass itself. Otherwise it would not be tight. And a crystal should be tight enough not to turn when the bezel is tight in the watch.

Snapping the crystal into the bezel is not a difficult trick, but it requires some practice and skill. First of all, the bezel being not entirely rigid, has a certain amount of "give". To fit the crystal, find the size that will go in and will not be tight. Then try the next higher size. Force one edge of the glass in. Hold the thumbs against the top of the glass and with the fingers expand the bezel slightly. Exert

Illustration 120—Sliding vernier gauge, inch and metric system. Measures accurately by means of the thumb actuated sliding vernier to 1/128 in. or 1/10 millimeter. Measures outside or inside and has depth slide and locking lever.

just enough pressure on the thumbs to force the glass into the bezel all around. Take care not to force it too much. If it is slightly too large, the edge may shatter with the force, and thus a crystal is ruined for future use. The fitting is much like a wheel is fitted into an automobile tire.

The crystal usually goes in with a distinct snap. Now try turning it in the bezel. If it does not turn with pressure from the fingers, it is probably right. Dampen and remove the label. See that the glass is clean from blemishes and foreign matter before placing the bezel on the watch.

Occasionally you will find an odd size bezel that you cannot fit tightly. One glass is just a little too small. The next one is a little too large. In a case of this kind, use the one nearest the correct size possible. Snap it in the bezel and run just a small bit of liquid crystal cement around the edge. This will seal it in the bezel and also prevent dust and trash entering around it.

Unusual Crystal Work

With the passing of hunting case watches, the geneva glass is little used today. However, there are still a few of these watches in use, and we must know how to handle one when we encounter it.

The hunting case watch is the closed case. To open the case you push the crown downward; this releases the spring catch. Another spring inside the case raises the lid. Underneath this lid is a very thin crystal fitted into a very thin, flimsy bezel.

This is known as the Geneva crystal. It ranges in sizes the same as the open face kind. Also it is numbered according to height. The number indicating the height is right underneath the size number. Height is indicated with a 5 or 6 or 7, or whatever the height may be. Six is a little higher than five. Seven a little higher than six, and so on.

In fitting the crystal there are several considerations in addition to the fitting of the crystal to the bezel. It must be high enough to permit freedom of the hands. Yet it must not be high enough to touch the lid of the watch when closed. If so, a slight pressure on the case will break the thin glass underneath. Often times in fitting one low enough to permit the lid free action, it is so low that it does not permit free action of the hands. Both points are important and must be watched carefully.

Secrets of Crystal Measurements

By far the larger part of the wrist watches in use today use the fancy shaped crystal. There are a total of some two thousand shapes and sizes. Naturally this requires considerable stock to be able to fit all crystals.

Since the fancy glass does not fit the bezel quite so snugly as the round glass, it is usually cemented in with some good grade cement made especially for that purpose.

The various shapes in fancy crystals are usually designated by a letter of the alphabet. Their sizes are designated by figures. In order to fit crystals quickly and profitably, you must first learn to measure the bezel to determine the size crystal you want. This is done as follows:

First, we must know how to measure the crystal. To do this we use a vernier gauge. (See illustration 120) The side next to you, as you hold the gauge as shown, is marked off in 1/10mm. The jaws next to you are made for measuring the OUTSIDE of objects. The points opposite are arranged to measure the INSIDE of things, such as watch bezels. The reading is the same. Examine the gauge a minute and you will understand how this can be.

The mm side of the gauge is numbered from 1 to 12. When reading this a naught is added; thus: 1 becomes 10, 2 becomes 20, etc. Millimeters are indicated on the base; fractions thereof are indicated in tenths on the sliding vernier. Now slide the vernier open until the extreme left hand line on the sliding vernier comes just past line 23. Then look at the lines on the sliding vernier and line up the 4th from the left with the line nearest it on the gauge. Now, if the first line on the left is past 20, plus 3 extra lines on the gauge, and has not yet reached the 4th extra line, then the reading is 234, which means 23 plus 4/10mm.

Next find the shape of the crystal in your crystal catalogue. Find any crystal bearing the number 234, omitting the two preceding numbers or letters. Slip that crystal between the jaws of the vernier, and see that it fits perfectly. Now try it on other crystals. Notice that each crystal has a series of numbers such as 6 C 234, if it is a Watch-Craft. If it is a BB crystal it will be C2346. If it is Perfit, it will probably be C234/6. Notice the figures are the same. The 234 actually means the length in millimeters. That is 23 plus 4/10 millimeters. The C designates the shape, according to the catalog. The 6 indicates the position in which it is found in that particular series of sizes. In other words, it is in sixth place in that series of numbers. There are or have been five other crystals which measured 234 in width.

Notice the use of the word width in the last sentence. Then notice that this crystal is also 234 mm wide. We know this by the secondary figures shown underneath the main number. It just so happens that the number selected here is the same length and width. Most crystals are not the same.

Now let's go back to the vernier gauge. Take a watch bezel. Place the points into the bezel and expand it at the ends until the blades of the point fit snugly into the bezel itself. What is the reading? Let us say it is exactly on 2; that is, the left line on the window of the slide stops exactly in line with line number 2 on the gauge. Not the second line, mind you, but the line numbered 2. In that case, the bezel would require a glass 20 mm long. Now measure the width in the same way, measuring at the widest point. Let us say the left hand line comes to within one and one half lines of the numbered 2 line. That would lack one and one half mm being 20mm, or 18 and one half mm. Let us see about that half. It is a half only if the 5th line on the sliding gauge lines up perfectly with a line on the main gauge. It will look like a half when reading the round numbers, but perhaps the 4th line is the one that lines up with the line on the main gauge. If so, the width is 18 and 4/10 mm.

Now by using the crystal catalog, find the letter indicating the shape of the bezel you are measuring. Then turn through your catalog until you find the crystal of that shape which measures 200 x 184. When you have found this, notice the full number and locate it in the cabinet. If you have measured accurately, it will fit.

Go over this procedure again and again until it is thoroughly fixed in your mind. Then it will not leave you.

Let me state here that not many watchmakers know how to read this gauge. They prefer to spend half an hour hunting for a crystal that may fit when they get through grinding on it. With this gauge and crystal catalog, you can fit any crystal in less than half the time it will take to look for it the other way. In short, it is the business way of doing it.

There are three poular brands of fancy glass crystals. They are Watch-Craft, B B, and Perfit. The numbering systems are all different; yet they are all the same. The letters are used to indicate the shape of the crystal.

Study your crystal catalog until you know the key letter for each shape. Then take your bezel measurements, locate the indicated size under that particular key letter, and it tells you the number of box in your cabinet holding that size glass, no matter which system you are using at the time.

How a Good System Increases Profit

For years it has been customary for jewelry stores and watch-makers everywhere to give a definite time guarantee on all watches sold and repaired. This is traditional, having been built up over a number of years. Originally, no doubt, it had some good points. Perhaps it still has. But the word guarantee has been so abused in recent years that all good, straight-thinking watchmakers would like to discard the guarantee, as we now know it. But it is so much a part of watch-making that you and I cannot change it. Therefore, we have to accept conditions as they are and make the most of them.

Perhaps in the years to come we shall find some other way to give the same good results without its attendant faults. It is well known that the "jack-leg" and the workman who has no intention of doing good work, even if he could, has in many instances out-guaranteed the best of workmen. He can give a longer, more inclusive guarantee than you, because he has no intention of making it good. For years he has done just that. Instead of the better workmen everywhere getting together and meeting this situation in the only way they could — abolishing the guarantee entirely — they play the "jack-legs" game by trying to live up to their guarantees.

As one instance in which the guarantee is made ridiculous, take the watch which is brought in for a Clean and Order job. The watch is properly repaired and put in good condition. It is delivered on Monday. The following Thursday the mainspring beaks. The owner brings it back. If he is honest and intelligent, he expects to pay for a spring and does so without grumbling. If he happens to be the kind who always wants something for nothing — and most likely he is, as we have all had that kind — he demands that you live up to your guarantee to keep the watch up for a twelve month period from the time of repairs.

Many times he knows he is not entitled to a free job, but is trying to save himself a few dollars by out-talking you. Occasionally he sincerely thinks that he is entitled to a free spring. In any event ,he knows that you have a good reputation to maintain, and that rather than have the ill will of a customer, you will do the job without charge.

Meantime the jackleg who can out-guarantee you seven ways for Sunday, will find several other things wrong with the watch and make enough charges to take care of the spring with a nice profit besides. He will get by with it because he has little reputation to lose one way or the other. And he does not mind misrepresenting the case if it is to his advantage to do so.

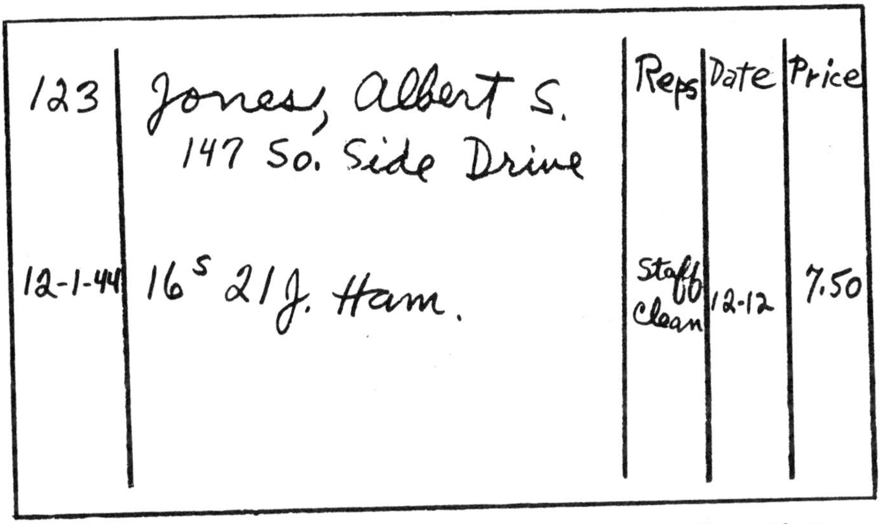

		Reps	Date	Price
123	Jones, Albert S. 147 So. Side Drive			
12-1-44	16^s 21 J. Ham.	Staff Clean	12-12	7.50

Illustration 121—File your repair records alphabetically on cards. Give watch an identification number (123) and write number on watch and on card. Same number will be used every time watch comes in.

This may not be a pretty picture I am drawing of the watchmaking industry. Frankly it is not. But what is more important — it is a very accurate picture. If you are to know the business, you must know its bad sides as well as its good sides. It is essential to know your competitors in order to know how to compete. Bear in mind that all your competitors are not bad. Some — perhaps the large majority — are strictly honest and straight-forward with their customers and fellow workmen. This kind you do not have to worry about.

Just try to be as upright yourself. But the jackleg, apparently, will always be with us. We cannot expose him. We can only regard him as a "horrible example" of what not to do in the watch-making business.

Now in order to give a guarantee that is honorable and fair, as well as intelligent, we must keep a record of all work done by us. In a few minutes we must be able to tell when we last repaired a watch, what was done to it, what was charged for the job, etc.

There are several methods of doing this. If you are doing only a minimum number of jobs, the repair record book will suffice. This simply lists the name, address of the customer, the kind of watch repairs done, date delivered, and the price charged. A number in the book should be the same as a number in the case, so as to facilitate finding the record in case the watch should come back for adjustment.

The above record is fairly complete. However, there is a much better record. This is the Card System. (See illustration 121)

In using the card system, the cards are kept alphabetically filed, and give a complete description of the watch. Also there is one number placed in the watch the first time it is brought in. That number is placed on the card for purposes of identification. No other number need ever be used.

Each time the job comes in, the date and extent of repairs needed are placed on the card. The date the watch is delivered is also placed on the card. Should it come back a few weeks later with some trouble such as a broken spring or the like, only a moment is required to look up the card and show the customer just what was done the last time, and what he or she paid. This will remove all doubt as to whether the job is covered by your guarantee. Most watchmakers guarantee a cleaning job for one year. If, through a faulty case it should have to be cleaned again before the twelve month period is up, they make a proportional charge to cover the time used. This is fair to both sides. Mainsprings are usually guaranteed one year. Staffs and most other parts are not guaranteed against breaking at all.

With the card system, then, you can immediately tell every time that particular watch has been in your shop, what was done to it each time and other pertinent information. Thus, at a glance you will know approximately what the watch needs before looking at it.

Prices vary according to location, class of store, quality of watch, what you think the customer will stand, and what you think your competitor will charge. This is as it is — but not as it should be. The better shops get good prices at all times. They never charge for more than they do. They charge a fair price for all they do. They do not cut prices, or try any cheap advertising schemes to bring "suckers" into their shops.

In fact, the honest workman who turns out consistently good work usually has so much work to do that he does not have to advertise. Certainly he does not have to resort to cheap advertising schemes. The public soon learns that it gets a square deal at that particular shop, and right thinking people appreciate that fact so much they go back again and again. Only in this way can you succeed.

On at least one other point, I should like to offer some pertinent advice. This has to do with the treatment of customers. Every person who comes into your store or shop is a potential customer. Cultivate him. On the customer your livelihood depends.

In being nice to a customer, you do not have to fawn upon him. Nor do you have to run over yourself trying to please him. He does not want this. All he wants is courteous, considerate treatment, and fair dealings at all times. He is certainly entitled to as much.

Salesmanship is part of being a good watch-maker. In fact it is perhaps your greatest asset, aside from your technical skill. If you are to work for someone else, first you must sell yourself to him in order to get the job. You must convince him that you have something. After you have done this, you simply have to produce. If you are going out for a job, either approach your employer by mail, or if you find a likely looking opportunity near home, go in to see him personally.

Your approach and appearance must be good. See that your clothes are clean, neatly pressed, shoes shined, and your general appearance good. Then ask for the Manager, or the Owner. Tell him what you want. Be direct and honest. State flatly what experience you have had. Do not go into details about how you got the experience. He is not interested in that. If you are not a finished workman, say so plainly and flatly. Let it be known that you want to start at or near the bottom with a chance to get more experience. Let the matter of salary come from the employer. He probably is willing to pay more than you would ask him. Let him know that all you want is a chance to show what you can do. Then do it. If it is understood that you get a raise in pay when you show what you can do, you will get it if you produce.

Remember that your employer is boss. His interest is your interest. Anything not to his interest is not to yours. If you work for a salary, give him a full days work every day. Do not try to take advantage of him. He will soon find you out.

Above all, be courteous to people with whom you work and with whom you come in contact. Do not try to impress others with your importance. You are not important to them. Only they are important to themselves. Learn something from everyone you meet. It can be done. You are now on your way up. You have a good start. Keep going.

If you write for a job, write a business-like letter. State facts clearly, succinctly. Do not overshoot yourself. Tell the prospective employer everything he needs to know, and no more. He is not interested in boring details. Make no statements you can not live up to. Give names and addresses of references. Enclose a stamped envelope.

The Watchmaster Rate Recorder

In recent years many machines have been introduced into watchmaking. The Cleaning machine and the Friction Jeweling tool, to name only two of the more important ones. These are outstanding machines that meant and will continue to mean much to watchmakers everywhere. They were accepted reluctantly. It meant a breaking down of traditions and habits of long standing. Watchmakers resented the change, to their ultimate sorrow.

Against their resistance, these new machines have gradually caught

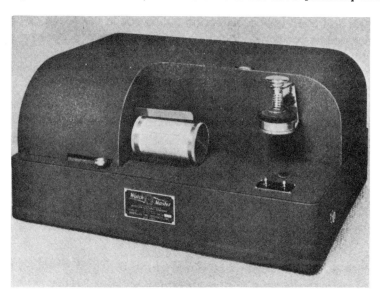

Illustration 122—The Watchmaster.

on and have helped to revolutionize watchmaking within our generation. They are now used by good workmen everywhere.

But perhaps the most outstanding, the most laudable, and perhaps the most universally needed machine of all is just now catching on after being kicked around for several years.

This machine is, of course, the Watchmaster. (See illustration 122) It is a product of Time Products Company, 580 Fifth Ave., New York.

To go into detail on the things this machine will do would require a book in itself. Since that is neither possible nor feasible here, our remarks shall be brief.

If possible to obtain one of these machines, do so. If not, then try to get employment where one is being used by workmen who understand it. For with the Watchmaster to work with, you will learn things that you could never learn without it.

You will learn how a watch may be out of beat, even though the "tick and the tock" may be of the exact duration so far as the ear can determine.

You will learn how the slight change in the hairspring may cause a big variation in time keeping.

You will learn how a hairspring out of true in the round or the flat, will not rate in positions. It can be out either way and the eye cannot detect it.

You will learn that regulator pins open too wide, or too close, will prevent accurate timing in both the short and long arcs.

The Watchmaster will show up trouble in thirty seconds that the trained eye and ear cannot detect in less than 24 hours.

It will enable you to regulate a watch in positions within a very few minutes, whereas from one day to a week is usually required.

It will show up escapement faults that neither the eye nor the ear can locate. These and many other things can be done with a Watchmaster.

Some of these claims may sound fantastic. They are not.

★   ★   ★   ★   ★

The end of this lesson is the end of the book. It must not be the end of your study period. If you are not entirely familiar with every lesson in the book, go back and repeat the performance over and over until you know it. You must do more than learn the words. Learn what they mean and how to perform the job they outline.

You have now reached the end of the beginning. If you know these lessons you are a watchmaker. But do not get too cocky. This book has just hit the high spots. There are many things worth knowing that could not be covered here. Things seldom needed such as pivoting staffs, pivoting train wheel pinions, replacing broken teeth in wheels, and many more. To be a finished workman you should know these things, even though you may never have to actually do one.

If you remain ever alert, you will never stop learning.

GOOD LUCK!

LESSON SIXTY-FIVE

Illustrated Supplement

Illustration 123—Balance cock bumper. Used for effecting change in balance cock or bridge.

Illustration 124—Alcohol blow torch for melting wax, alloys and metals.

Illustration 125—Soldering torch. For sizing rings (illustrated) repairing chains and soldering metal of all kinds.

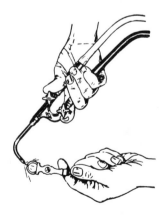

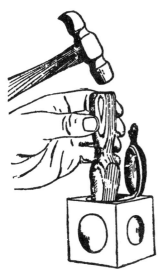

Illustration 127—Bench drill.

Illustration 126—Case straightening and dent removing.

Illustration 128—Hand drill with chuck.

Illustration 130—Ring holder. For work to be done on inside surface such as engraving, filing, ruling, polishing, etc.

Illustration 129—Curved point graver with handle.

Illustration 131 — Clock hand remover. Hands on inexpensive clocks (being driven on) are hard to remove without a special tool.

Illustration 132—Pallet clip. For holding parts of movement in position while assembling.

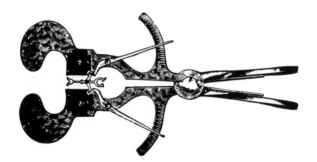

Illustration 133 — Pallet stone setter and adjusting tool. Prevents damage to jewels or lever. Holds them rigid and level.

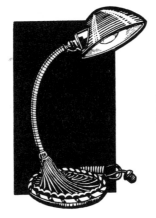

Illustration 134—Bench lamp.
Inexpensive model used by
most watchmakers.

Illustrations 135 to 138—Cement
chuck for staff making and pivoting. Chuck has tapered end,
hollowed out to a point for
automatically centering staff.
Sealing wax or cement is heated over an alcohol lamp and
placed in hollowed end. Staff
is then inserted into cement and
is spun true in lathe while cement is hardening.

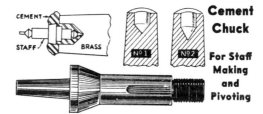

**Cement
Chuck**

**For Staff
Making
and
Pivoting**

Illustration 139—Clock level,
pocket size, for leveling
clock shelf, etc.

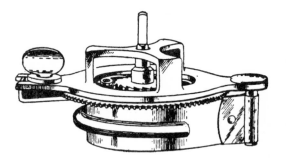

Illustration 140—Clock main-spring winder.

Illustration 141—Rectangular movement holder.

Illustration 142—Chuck pin vise. Hollow handle permits wires, broaches, etc., to be inserted and held in chuck jaws at any desired position.

Illustration 143—Second hand pliers. For use in holding second hands while enlarging them with a broach, or for making the hole in socket smaller.

Illustration 144—Bench vise. Inexpensive screw clamp vise with 1½ inch jaws. Opens to 2 inches.

Illustration 145—Window electric clock. Many watchmakers
make substantial extra profits
selling display clocks to mer-
chants. Good advertising for
the merchant, good business for
the watchmaker.

Illustrations 146, 147, 148,
—Baby Ben Quiet Move-
ment alarm clock.

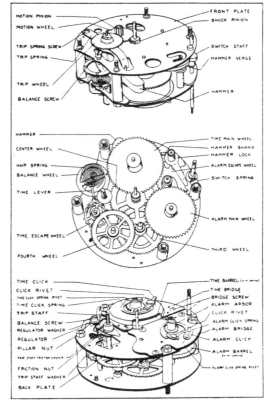

LESSON SIXTY-SIX

Self-Help Notes

Index